John Milne

the man who mapped the shaking earth

Paul Kabrna

CRAVEN & PENDLE
GEOLOGICAL SOCIETY

Copyright

Published by Craven & Pendle Geological Society
First Edition, 2007

Copyright © Paul Kabrna, 2007

Typeset in Adobe Caslon Pro
Printed and bound by *The City Press Leeds Ltd.*
St. Ann's Mill, Commercial Road, Kirkstall, Leeds LS5 3AE

British Library Cataloguing in Publication Data
A catalogue record for this book is available from the British Library

ISBN 978-0-9555289-0-3

For Yvonne James

About the Author

Paul Kabrna graduated as a teacher of geology at Crewe & Alsager College of Higher Education. In 1970 he joined the North East Lancashire Group of the Geologists' Association serving as Chairman for two years and Joint Editor of the NELGGA Proceedings from 1985 to 1990. In 1989 he joined the Yorkshire Geological Society serving on the council from 1991 as Circular Editor for 11 years and as Web Editor for 3 years. Paul, along with his wife, Yvonne James and Paul Wignall of Leeds University, founded Craven & Pendle Geological Society in 1990.

Fig. 1 The author relaxing in The John Milne pub, Milnrow, Rochdale (2006). On the wall is a portrait of John Milne (left) and Milne family photographs (right). Credit: Yvonne James, 2006

email: Paul_Kabrna@msn.com   www.cpgs.org.uk

"The phenomena of earthquakes are at once his serious study and his delightful occupation. For him the earth is like an Aeolian harp, it vibrates to the influence of every heavenly body, it is played upon by the sun's tropic rays, buffeted by the unruly ocean in its lap, resounds to the stress of the storm-winds, is shaken by earthquakes and volcanoes from pole to pole, yet repeats, by a tender throb to his seismometer at Shide, the faintest vibration even from a distance of twelve thousand miles away."

Eminent Living Geologists: John Milne
Geological Magazine, Vol. 9, No. 578, August 1912

"Seismologists in the UK have continued to play an important role in the development of the subject throughout the 20th century. This was especially true in the earlier part of the century, when global earthquake monitoring was effectively the responsibility of one man, John Milne."

R.M.W. Musson (British Geological Survey) 2003

Contents

Illustrations

Acknowledgements

My wife, Yvonne, encouraged me to accept the challenge of writing this brief account of the life and work of John Milne, knowing full well what would be involved. The author is deeply indebted to Patrick A. Nott for his support, for writing the Foreword, and for providing photographs from his Isle of Wight personal collection (Figs. 40, 47, 49, 52, 54).

My thanks to Andrew James for technical advice on type setting, print preparation, and for producing the front and back cover artwork. Kate James was no help at all with this project but did supply much needed coffee refills! The author is grateful to Professor Paul Wignall, Dr. Richard Twitchett and Ann Hampson for reading a draft of the manuscript and offering their advice and comments.

I would also like to thank the following for allowing the inclusion of illustrations in their possession or for which they hold the copyright:

Yvonne James, Craven & Pendle Geological Society:
The John Milne pub (Fig. 1 and Fig. 2), *Rock Pillars, Rochdale Cemetery* (Fig. 3), *Milne Family Tree* (Fig. 4), *Stonyhurst College Observatory* (Fig. 50).

Local Studies, Touchstones Rochdale, MBC:
Drake Street in 1904 (Fig. 5).

W. A. Montevecchi, Memorial University of Newfoundland:
Funk Island (Fig. 8).

NASA Johnson Space Centre:
Newfoundland (Fig. 7)   *Sinai Peninsula* (Fig. 10)   *Milne Volcano* (Fig. 26).

Vladimir Kroupnik, Perth, Western Australia:
Nizhniy Tagil, Lena Goldfield, Irkutsk (Figs. 13 to 17) from the book *The Russian Gold* (Moscow, 1994).

Shun Nakano, Institute of Geology and Geoinformation, Geological Survey of Japan:
Ōshima volcano (Figs. 19, 20, and 21).

Alexander Belousov, Institute of Volcanology, Petropavlovsk, Kamchatsky, Russian Federation:
Paramushir Island (Fig. 24).
Ebeko Volcano on Paramushir (Fig. 25).

Tomomi Shibahara of Nagasaki University Library:
Meiji Period photographs of the Mino-Owari earthquake, Mt. Asama, Mt. Fuji, Great Buddha of Kamakura, Ainu (Figs. 22, 27, 30, 31, 32, 33, 37, and 43).

Yutaka Honda, Tohoku University, Department of Earth Science, Mie University, Tsu, Japan:
Neodani Fault Scarp (Fig. 34).
Earthquake Observation Museum (Fig. 35).

Nolan C. Evangelista, Philippine Institute of Volcanology and Seismology:
Neodani Fault trench inside the Earthquake Observation Museum (Fig. 36).

The Seismological Society of America:
John & Toné Milne, Shide Hill House garden (Fig. 39).
John Milne and Toné Milne, Shide Hill House (Fig. 48).

Kaori Kurita, Madrid, Spain:
Mount Asama (Fig. 23).

Science & Society Picture Library, Science Museum, London:
Milne Horizontal Pendulum Seismograph, 1899 (Fig. 42).

Jonathan Clatworthy, Lapworth Museum of Geology, Birmingham University:
The Milne-Shaw Seismograph (Fig. 55 - 60).

Foreword

Forgotten for a time on the Isle of Wight

The first full biography "*John Milne: the Father of Modern Seismology*" came to be written in effect by accident. Early in the 1970's Leslie Herbert-Gustar, who sadly died a few years ago, and I were intending to write a history of Isle of Wight technology. We decided to start with John Milne, then known only to us as a name, simply because we thought there may still be a few older individuals alive who had met him and we might possibly get a paragraph or two as part of a chapter in the history.

Many circumstances had led to his life and international work being nearly completely forgotten on the Isle of Wight. He died just before the First World War, Toné his wife returned to Japan in 1919, they had no children, the observatory-related matters had been transferred to Oxford, Shide Hill House their Isle of Wight home since 1895 was sold with much of the site then built on and even the main part of the house left to decay before demolition. Coupled with the fact we have had no earthquakes lately, an ever increasing population mobility and the Island's innate propensity to undervalue its considerable contribution to science and technology, his memory was by the time we started our research all but erased.

Fortunately we were able to find and interview several who knew him and Toné quite well. Four boxes of 'goodies' such as school reports and unpublished material in his dreadful handwriting, some singed by the fire in Japan were located in the local record office. Carisbrooke Castle Museum we found had hundreds of uncatalogued black and white negatives. We obtained from a number of people several boxes of his hand painted magic lantern slides. Like all biographical researchers we made many mad dashes across the country to meet contacts and spend long hours in many libraries and archives to publish some seven years later.

But research can have its funnier moments. Leslie and I, over the same weekend but quite independently, discovered where his grave was located and wishing to impress the other each decided to check it out first – we both arrived at the churchyard gate at the same time! It also has its lucky breaks. Working in the old British Museum Reading Room I noticed written in pencil on a Milne paper just above his name 'Mark Kershaw' and it was this find that led to the discovery of the 'railway station bookstall' fiction he had written under this pseudonym. In the 1970's 'plant a tree' was in vogue and we decided that this might be a good way to honour Milne. Jokingly we said 'why do all the hard work ourselves?' and this led to the then Japanese Ambassador unveiling plaques and planting cherry saplings in Newport taken from the site of Milne's college in Tokyo. It cemented good relationships, ensured Milne featured in the pamphlet issued on the Queen's visit to Japan, an edition of our biography in Japanese, several interviews with NHK, the magic lantern slides featuring on TV and in newspapers in Japan. John would have appreciated it for he even got a slot on Blue Peter and John Craven's *Newsround*.

What we slowly uncovered as we got to know John Milne better, was that he was much more than just a foreign lecturer, mining engineer, geologist and seismologist. Here was one of the great Victoria pioneers, a person so much larger than life, driven by immense enthusiasm, extremely generous and kind-hearted, interested in people of every background, full of fun with a great sense of humour and somewhat a little mischievous at heart.

John Milne was proud of his roots and never lost his Lancastrian accent. This with his cigarette-burnt hat identified him for many we met. He by no means ever wanted to hide from his Rochdale childhood whether at the then posh Royal Victoria Yacht Club which he regularly visited either to measure the tidal tilt of Ryde Sands, just to enjoy its good whisky, or perhaps see if the 'activity' of the steward and housekeeper sharing the same time off appeared again on his seismograms. We were told frequently he was always the same; be it at the golf club, delivering a Royal Society prestigious lecture or a local university extension one. His accent contrasted well with the Isle of Wight local dialect, as too did Toné's broken English and the diversification of culture it brought to the then hamlet of Shide. Just how much Japanese John read or spoke we were unable to find out.

Their social life ranged from visiting Osborne House where Toné remembered Queen Victoria helping her on with her coat. They regularly hosted at Shide important visitors, international scientists or just groups like the local photographic society, but all were equally welcome even boys scrumping. One lad at the time recalls when caught Toné would give them a little apple, John as many as they could carry. Just how many of the visitors saw his numbered sequence of single railway tickets starting at 00001 from Charring Cross to

Shide Station is not known, but it illustrates his love of the light-hearted and highlights the slight but attractive eccentricity he had.

From what we learnt many years back talking to those older members of the Island community, John Milne would have much appreciated a pub named after him here as at Rochdale, where the old thatched Barley Mow was his local. Still Newport does have his grave, bits of the old Shide Hill House estate such as the laboratory building, part now called Milne House and the lodge, cherry trees planted in remembrance and a Milne Way cul-de-sac nearby; I think he would have preferred blind-alley.

Leslie Herbert-Gustar and I were greatly helped and much encouraged when writing by John Wartnaby who first recorded the life of John Milne in his MSc dissertation. Hence it is now a real pleasure to welcome this new work keeping a great Victorian's memory alive by Paul Kabrna. For this book takes the opportunity to develop, amongst other things, more of his geological interests as well as the connections with Lancashire and particularly Rochdale. Three decades later the text and illustrations well supplement "*John Milne: the Father of Modern Seismology*" with its emphasis on Milne's life at Shide on the Isle of Wight, his wide range of activities and the wealth of the resulting publications. Once again there is currently another scholarly work in print celebrating the first, even if emeritus, *Professor of Seismology*.

Patrick A. Nott

Preface

Compared to most distinguished British pioneers of geology such as James Hutton, William Smith, and Adam Sedgwick, the life and work of John Milne (1850-1913) is not particularly well known in his home country. If you are indeed aware of him, it is most likely through his contribution in developing the seismograph during his time in Japan in the late 19th century. Partly because of this, John Milne became known as the *'Father of Modern Seismology'*. They even called him *'Earthquake Milne'*. He was a hero in Japan and lauded around the world although nowadays he's generally remembered only by seismologists. If you delve a little deeper into his life and work you will come to realise just what a polymorph he was.

In writing this book it is my intention to develop his geological achievements and at the same time celebrate Milne's life by tracing his footsteps from his family roots in Rochdale where his enquiring mind was nurtured. Prizes and awards gained at school and college reflect an enthusiastic and diligent approach to education. Milne's adventurous nature began to manifest itself in his early teenage years and stayed with him throughout his life. Early accomplishments did not go unnoticed by the scientific community, some of whom had no hesitation in nominating young Milne for important expeditions abroad during college days and thereafter.

Milne's academic standing, together with his exploits as a field geologist specialising in mineralogy and mining on international expeditions, attracted the attention of the Meiji government of Japan who were looking to hire foreign scientists and technicians, mostly from Europe, some from the United States as teachers / lecturers. Hence, at the age of 25, Milne was offered a position as Professor of Mining and Geology at their newly formed Imperial College of Engineering in Tokyo. He accepted the offer and then had to decide on how he would travel to Tokyo. For most intrepid travellers a long sea-voyage was the obvious option. Milne however didn't care for sea voyages as he was prone to sea-sickness. After thoughtful consideration, he surprised his colleagues and friends by announcing that he planned to take the overland route to Japan through Scandinavia, Russia, Siberia, Mongolia and China.

Fig. 2 *The John Milne pub, Newhay Road, Milnrow, Rochdale. Lancashire.*
Credit: Yvonne James, 2006

Many of his friends thought Milne foolish for considering such an unduly long and hazardous route through relatively unfamiliar territory.

During his tenure in Japan he gained a reputation of being a hard working *oyatoi-gaikokujin* (honourable foreign hireling) with a healthy spirit of adventure and appetite for field work. When the opportunity arose he would set off on expeditions to visit interesting volcanoes initially on Honshū. Milne also developed an interest in archaeology and the origins of the Japanese people which eventually led him to the city of Hakodate on the northern island of Hokkaido. He did so much more than just guide the development of the seismograph and seismology during his time in Japan.

After twenty years in Japan (and partly due to circumstances beyond his control) Milne returned to England and settled on the Isle of Wight with his wife Toné Milne and his trusted assistant Shinobu 'Snowy' Hirota. Much of his time was spent in furthering the development of the seismograph and the establishment of a worldwide seismological network. For a while at least, the Isle of Wight was the world centre of earthquake-related studies with Milne becoming the driving force behind the British Association for the Advancement of Science (BAAS) Seismological Investigation Committee. John Milne remained the Secretary of this committee until his death in 1913, aged 62.

Milne always considered himself a 'Rochdale lad' and was proud of the fact that he retained his Lancashire accent. He was particularly at home when in conversation with friends and colleagues, many of whom fondly remembered Milne for his infectious sense of humour. He was a man who succeeded in seeing his life's work, the study of seismology, obtain a foremost place in the physical sciences.

By bringing the story of Professor John Milne to a wider public it is my hope that his life and work will be appreciated by all, and more importantly, not forgotten.

Chapter 1

Setting the Scene

Located north-east of Manchester, Rochdale lies on the southern edge of the Rossendale Fells. The Peak District is to the south-east and to the east the central Pennines. The River Roch flows through the centre of Rochdale and in Milne's time could be forded at the bottom of Drake Street.

In the mid to late nineteenth century Rochdale was a typical mill town specialising in wool manufacture, cotton spinning, and weaving. In 1844 at 33 Toad Lane the 'Co-operative Movement' was born. Unbeknown to the Rochdale Pioneers, their organisation would eventually reach out to all parts of the world. Even though Rochdale's colourful history is well documented, two aspects of its geological heritage in Milne's time are certainly worthy of mention:

1) About half a mile south-west of Rochdale Town Hall at Sparth Bottoms, a local fossil collector in 1903 unearthed a new species of Carboniferous scorpion from a clay-ironstone nodule which had been extracted from a shale bed 135 feet above the Arley Mine coal seam. The scorpion measured 74 mm in length and differed from other described Carboniferous scorpions by virtue of its more 'graceful form'. Walter Baldwin and William Henry Sutcliffe, in discussion with Mr. A. W. Parker of Rochdale who found the scorpion, decided to name it *Eoscorpius sparthensis* after Sparth Bottoms from where it was first found. In April 1904, Baldwin & Sutcliffe presented their find to the Geological Society of London. They described where the scorpion had been found, what it looked like, and the geological significance of the discovery.

2) In the particularly unlikely setting of Rochdale Cemetery on Bury Road you can still see what may be one of the earliest geological trails in the UK (1855). The trail was constructed by two local men, James Horsfall & Robert Law. It takes the form of around 30 rock pillars (geological tombstones) about 3 to 4 feet high arranged in such a way as to mark the boundaries of the burials of Church of England, Roman Catholic, and Nonconformists denominations

Fig. 3 *A variety of rock pillars to be found in Rochdale Cemetery. The entrance to the cemetery is on the B6222 Bury Road adjacent to the B6452 Sandy Lane.*
Credit: Yvonne James, 2006

within the cemetery. The pillars attracted the attention of the distinguished geologist Professor Sir William Boyd-Dawkins (1837-1929) who described the trails geological significance before congratulating the local corporation in 1881 on the completion of a remarkable and interesting endeavour.

The majority of pillars represent common sedimentary rocks of which Wenlock limestone of Silurian age is one example. There are a few examples of igneous rocks such as basalt from the Giant's Causeway in Northern Ireland and Red and Grey granite from Aberdeen. Metamorphic rocks are also present as noted by white marble from Carrara, Italy. Many of the rock specimens especially those of sedimentary origin are badly weathered.

Family History

John Milne's father, (also named John Milne as it was the custom of the day to give sons their father's name), and his wife Emma, daughter of James Twycross of Wokingham, lived in Rochdale. His grandfather was also named

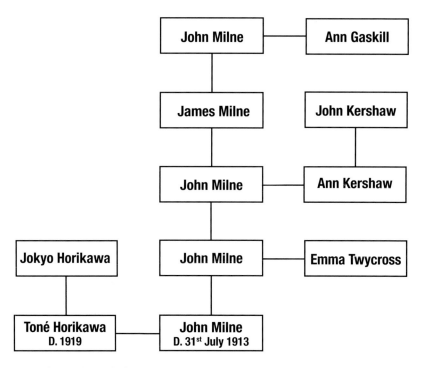

Fig. 4 Part of John Milne's Family Tree. Credit: Yvonne James, 2006

John Milne and he married Ann Kershaw the daughter of John Kershaw of Claylane. The Milne family have been native to Rochdale and the surrounding area for centuries. One of the earliest records of Milne's residing in Milnrow, Rochdale dates back as far as 1626.

Milne's father was a successful wool merchant. He journeyed to Liverpool with his wife Emma who at the time was expecting their first child. On a cold winters night, John was born at Mount Vernon, in the Edge Hill district of Liverpool on the 30th December 1850.

When John was 3 weeks old the family returned to their Rochdale home at 147 Drake Street. Three months later they returned to Liverpool for young John's christening on the 2nd March 1851 at St. John's Church (1783-1887). In 1904 the former site of the church was opened to the public as a terraced garden area known today as St. John's Garden.

In an article in the *Rochdale Times* in 1910 Professor Milne recollects his early years in Rochdale: *"I remembered 147 Drake Street. I remembered a back bedroom with a skylight in the ceiling, my mother titivating herself at a looking glass, and I standing at the back dressed in a velvet petticoat and a hat with ostrich plumes,*

Fig. 5 Open-topped tram in Drake Street, 1904.
Credit: Local Studies, Touchstones, Rochdale, Rochdale MBC.

Fig. 6 *John Milne lived at 147 Drake Street, (first from the left): Photo taken 2006.*

ready for exhibition to our neighbours. A tall thing and surrounded by curtains stood beneath the skylight. I clambered inside and pulled a string I found. The queer thing with curtains turned out to be a shower bath. I was not taken out for the exhibition. For years afterwards I never even pulled a bell handle."

Eventually the Milne family moved to more comfortable surroundings of Tunshill House. Although Tunshill Farm still exists today adjacent to the M62 motorway, I haven't been able to locate Tunshill House as it was probably demolished to make way for the M62.

Young Milne had an inquisitive mind and was not afraid to ask questions, so it probably came as a relief, especially to his mother, when he reached school age. Miss Fisher, a teacher at the mixed school on Milkstone Road just off Drake Street, was responsible for guiding young John's academic progress. Judging by the awards and prizes that came his way he must have been an enthusiastic hard working student. One of his first prizes was a book called 'The Guide to Knowledge'. Milne's recollection of this in later life suggests that he drew inspiration from having received this book.

High school education began at Liverpool College Middle School. Young Milne worked hard and the rewards continued. On one occasion he received prize money which he used to fund a visit to the Lake District of Northern England. Most youngsters would no doubt have been satisfied to have explored the splendour of the Lakes and just returned home. Milne, on the other hand wanted his adventure to continue so he crossed the Irish Sea with the intention of exploring the city of Dublin and the region immediately to the south. He was obviously a resourceful young man because he took to playing the piano in pubs along the way in order to make a little extra money.

In later years on the Isle of Wight Milne often reflected on his life in Rochdale by enthusiastically reminiscing about memorable moments such as time spent with his two favourite shire horses, 'Rushbearing' and 'Old Ben' who pulled the carrier's wagon. The horses would drive young Milne from the Red Lion to the Tim Bobbin when on his way home to Tunshill. He also recalls the not *too* memorable visits to the local barber's shop to have his hair curled.

The family moved to the London area where they are known to have lived in the boroughs of Hounslow and Richmond amongst other places. Why they moved to the London area is unknown. Nevertheless the opportunity for travelling still burned bright in Milne as noted by his first visit to France. He enjoyed his leisure time especially when he was accompanied by his dog and / or sailing in his canoe which he named *Ranger*.

At the age of seventeen Milne obtained a place in the Department of Applied Sciences at King's College, University of London. The courses that he undertook included: Mathematics, Manufacturing Arts, Mechanics, Geology, Mineralogy, Geometric Drawing, Surveying and Divinity. Receiving awards was a trend that continued even at King's College. Bearing in mind that Milne's academic interest was rooted in science, he was in fact honoured with a special award of an A.K.C. (Associate of King's College) for Divinity.

Geology and mineralogy had by now become his main scientific interest and at the age of 21 he was still eager to further his knowledge and experiences. An early opportunity came his way when he teamed up with fellow geologist and mining engineer and friend William Lord Watts (b. 1850). The two of them set sail for Iceland in a Danish steamer with the intention of exploring the great glacier Vatnajökull (literally Lake Glacier) located in the south-east of the island. Milne also took advantage of this opportunity to observe Iceland's geysers and Mount Hekla, the most famous and one of the most scientifically informative volcanoes on Iceland. On their return to London, Milne revealed their findings in a lecture he gave to the Engineering Society of King's College. In his lecture he described, amongst other things, the difficult wet conditions of the expedition and the untapped wealth of sulphur deposits.

As for William Watts, he returned to Iceland in 1875 as leader of a six-man expedition to make a more thorough exploration of the '*Jökulls, or ice mountains and fjalls*'. His decision to make the trek may have been influenced by the violent eruption of the volcano Askja on the 4th January 1875 which at that time was relatively unknown. Both Watts and Milne shared the same eager (though some may say reckless) determination to face hazardous situations head-on. In the case of Watt's, a good example of his carefree approach to observational science comes from his notes taken at Askja in the summer of 1875: "*...beneath us lay a pandemonium of steam and hideous sounds ... the most hideous shrieks, groans, booming and screaming sounds rose from all parts of this terrible depression, the bottom of which was now utterly obscured. The sides of the crater were evidently falling in, and huge wide cracks, even where we stood, showed us that our position was not altogether a safe one. So we lit our pipes and waited until we could obtain a better view.*"

Milne undertook further study as a mining engineer at the prestigious Royal School of Mines in London. Under the watchful eye of Warington Smythe (1817-1890) Milne visited the mining districts of Lancashire, Cornwall and later Central Europe, where he studied mineralogy at the University of Freiberg and visited principal German mining districts.

The profile of John Milne was beginning to grow, particularly amongst fellow academics. With his education complete, he didn't have long to wait before he was offered his first contract of employment for two years (1873-74) investigating mineral resources of Newfoundland as a member of an expedition team under the leadership of Cyrus Field. Midway through his contract with Cyrus Field, Milne had the time and the opportunity to participate in an expedition sent out by the Royal Geographical Society. For this he was recruited as geologist in Dr. Charles Tilstone Beke's expedition to the Sinai desert (1874). The purpose of the expedition was to fix the exact location of Mount Sinai.

The next chapter documents Milne's extensive travels up to and including his epic journey to Japan in 1875 where he was to become Professor of Geology and Mining at the newly formed Imperial College of Engineering at Tokyo — a position that would dictate the future course of his life.

Chapter 2

The Long and Winding Road

Expedition 1: Newfoundland and the Great Auk

Cyrus W. Field (1819-1892), an American financier and entrepreneur, is particularly well known for playing a key role in the successful laying of the first transatlantic under-sea cable in 1858. In 1873 Cyrus Field wanted to hire an able mining geologist to accompany him to Newfoundland in search of coal and mineral resources, so he contacted the *Royal School of Mines* and they recommended Milne for the task.

The expedition took place during the summers of 1873 and 1874. Milne thoroughly explored all parts of Newfoundland — the relatively unknown inland region and as many coastal bays and coves as he could gain access to. His assessment of Newfoundland's rocks, their formation and mineralogy, was fully described in two scientific papers published in the Journal of the Geological Society in 1874. With his previous experience of Iceland in mind, Milne considered his visit to Newfoundland an ideal opportunity to further his understanding of the processes related to the interaction of ice and rock. He observed many icebergs (a common occurrence in Newfoundland's Atlantic waters) focusing particularly on the factors that affected their floating and stability. In comparing the two areas of study, Milne concluded that coastal ice seemed to be more effective as a rock transporting agent than icebergs. His observations on all ice-related matters were later published in the Geological Magazine and the Journal of the Geological Society.

Whilst Milne was in Newfoundland, he visited a remote uninhabited desolate rocky outcrop known as Funk Island to search for evidence of the extinct Great Auk or *Pinguinus impennis* (*Alca impennis* in Milne's day). Milne's exploration of Funk Island is fully described in his publication *Relics of the Great Auk* (1875). Historically, the Great Auk, also known as garefowl (from the old Norse geirfugl), or penguin in other references, used to breed on the island and some believe it may have been its last resting place. This fact alone was enough to convince Milne to make the visit.

Fig. 7 *Newfoundland and Funk Island*
Adapted from http://veimages.gsfc.nasa.gov/3676/Newfoundland.A2002210.1415.250m.jpg
Credit: Jacques Descloitres, MODIS Land Rapid Response Team, NASA/GSFC

Fig. 8 *Funk Island: home to Gannets, Auks and Murres: Credit: W. A. Montevecchi*

- 9 -

Funk Island (*Fig. 8*) lies approximately 60 kilometres (38 miles) from Cape Freels, one of the eastern headlands of Newfoundland. From north-east to south-west it is just under a kilometre (½ mile) long. Running east to west the width of the island is about half a kilometre (¼ mile). The island has no beaches, so to gain access Milne had to scramble up a small cliff. Navigating around the small island was easy because it is nearly flat with maximum elevation above sea level of only 14 metres. He described the composition

Fig. 9 *The Great Auk*
Taken from Relics of the Great Auk . (After Milne, 1875)

of the rock on which Funk Island is made out of as being highly feldspathic pinkish granite with a small quantity of black mica. The observed similarity to rocks on mainland Newfoundland prompted him to suggest a probable Laurentian geological age.

Milne's desire to secure some relics of the Great Auk was limited to about one hour due to the likelihood of hazardous rising winds and high tidal swells. Many bones surfaced during the early part of the search but none that could have been identified as belonging to the Great Auk. Nevertheless good fortune smiled on Milne when in a small grassy hollow the beak of a Great Auk was discovered. A little more digging revealed a substantial cache of bones of at least fifty birds. Milne considered how these bones may have come to be accumulated in such a manner before tentatively suggesting that *"they may have died peacefully or they were the remains of some great slaughter where the birds had been killed, parboiled, and despoiled only of their feathers, after which they were just thrown in a heap."* In his opinion a combination of factors probably conspired to bring about the Great Auk's downfall and eventual extinction. Firstly, the Great Auk was an excellent swimmer but could not fly (unlike other auks). Secondly, they only reared one young at a time. Thirdly, the Great Auk was easily hunted by man.

The visit to Funk Island must have pressed Milne's 'need to know more button' about the extinction of the Great Auk because his published scientific paper, *Relics of the Great Auk*, includes a comprehensive collection of facts relating to the bird from five other geographical regions as listed below:

I.   North and North-Eastern Europe
II.   Great Britain
III.   The Faroe Isles
IV.   Iceland
V.   North America and Greenland

In Milne's publication the facts related to each region are listed in chronological order. He states that in Great Britain, the first record is a prehistoric reference to the remains of two Great Auks found in kitchen middens of Caithness. The last British record of 1845 reports the sighting of a pair in Belfast Bay. On the information that he gathered in Newfoundland, the last of these birds seems to have disappeared around 1845. From the geographical list it was clear to Milne that the Great Auk was never so far north as the arctic regions. In fact the boundaries of its home territory appear to have been marked out rather by isothermal lines than by those of latitude. Other naturalists of the time believed that the Great Auk may still be living on some desolate uninhabited island off Newfoundland, however, Milne held little hope that this may be the case. Milne quotes from Charles Kingsley's *Water Babies* in which reference was made to the garefowl. The inclusion of this demonstrates Milne's disapproval of the needless destruction of wildlife by man.

Funk Island has operated as a wildlife reserve since 1964 and from 1983 it was designated Funk Island Ecological Reserve. The island is protected from all unauthorized human activity although enforcing this has proved challenging for the authorities concerned.

Expedition 2: The Sinai Peninsula

Prior to completing his Newfoundland commitment (he was contracted to undertake two summers work), Milne was recommended to take part in an expedition sent out by the Royal Geographical Society under the leadership of Dr. Charles Tilstone Beke (1800-1874), an explorer and biblical scholar. Professor Tennant, a senior member of the Royal Geographical Society and one of Milne's former lecturers, had no hesitation in recommending Milne for this task. As Charles Beke was 73 years old he needed someone younger and physically capable of climbing mountains in order for him to complete his mission which was to ascertain the true location of Mount Sinai. In the Old Testament, Mount Sinai is the place where the Law had been presented to Moses. Dr. Beke was convinced that the true Mount Sinai was in fact Jebel Baghir which he believed to be an extinct volcano located north east of Akaba. The traditional site amongst many other biblical scholars for Mount Sinai is the mountain Jebel Musa (literally 'Mountain of Moses') located on the Sinai peninsula not far from Tor in the Gulf of Suez. Milne was not particularly interested in the biblical aspect of the expedition, however, the opportunity of adding to his geological knowledge he felt was too good to miss.

The expedition left Folkestone on the 8th December 1873. The age gap between the two of them wasn't a problem at all; in fact the old explorer and young Milne got along exceedingly well and became good friends. They journeyed to the French capital Paris and then on to Turin and Venice in Italy where they boarded the P & O steamship *Simla* for their sea voyage across the Mediterranean to Alexandria and then overland to Cairo, Egypt. In Cairo they were delayed until Dr. Beke obtained, from the Khêdive of Egypt, safe conduct and a boat for their journey to Akaba. Milne made the most of his time by visiting the great pyramids and museums. Dr. Beke wrote the following in his diary: *"I shall be glad to get away from here on Milne's account as well as my own. He wants to be actively employed. Having used up all the geological facts that this bare region presents to him, he is now hard at work studying Arabic, Italian and French."*

After a delay of nearly a month, the Khêdive sent written permission and provided transport for the expedition to continue. On crossing the Nile delta to Suez they met up with a man called Hashim who was to be their guide. Together they continued on to their boat named the *Erin* which proved to be somewhat unreliable. The journey down the Gulf of Suez included a visit to Tor but no attempt on Jebel Musa was made. The expedition crossed the

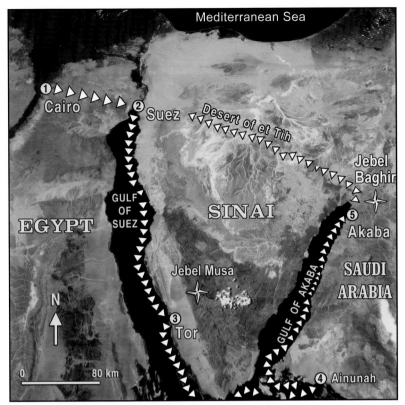

Fig. 10 *The route and place names are based on Milne's sketch published in Dr. Charles W. Beke's expedition report.*

Image courtesy of the Image Science & Analysis Laboratory, NASA Johnson Space Centre: (http://eol.jsc.nasa.gov). Mission: ISS013 Roll: E Frame: 15190 Mission ID on the Film or image: ISS013

Gulf of Akaba to Ainunah where Dr. Beke informed Milne that he believed the Israelites had camped there 3 000 years ago. Whenever the *Erin* anchored en-route Milne always went ashore to explore and make notes on the local geology. He also collected many fossils during this expedition.

On their arrival at Akaba at the head of the gulf, members of the expedition plus the son of a local sheikh were assembled and camels provided for their journey across the desert. They set up camp for the night at the foot of Jebel Baghir. Even though Dr. Beke was satisfied that they were in the right place, Jebel Baghir or his 'Mount Sinai' did not quite live up to his expectations and appeared not to be a volcano at all. Milne was given the task next day to climb the mountain and make a thorough investigation of the summit in order to determine whether it was of volcanic origin.

The next morning Milne and his team began their trek to the summit. Dr. Beke was full of admiration for Milne and was anxious to give him credit for his admirable contribution to his expedition. Hashim the guide and the Sheikh's son also accompanied Milne who departed base camp riding the Sheikh's horse. They made their way along a narrow wadi but had to leave the horses at the head of the gorge with two Arabs before beginning their ascent to the summit. As they climbed the mountain the weather became increasingly bitter and cold enough for snow from previous snowfalls to be present. At the summit they found horns and skulls of slaughtered animals but more importantly, based on the geological evidence, Milne confidently announced that Jebel Baghir was definitely not a volcano. There were boulders of granite at the summit which caught Milne's attention, partly because they held inscriptions which he attempted to make sense of. Regrettably, Milne had to return with disappointing news for Dr. Beke.

During their descent down the far side of Jebel Baghir, the expedition encountered some Bedouins. Thinking that the Sheikh was coming, the Bedouins invited Milne and members of the expedition to dine with them. For the feast they killed, prepared, and cooked a lamb. However, this experience with the Bedouins did not gain favour with Milne as he was critical of the filth, the tent, and the smoke. Nevertheless he had the good sense to keep his thoughts to himself as he certainly didn't want to offend anyone.

Having returned to base camp in the late afternoon, Dr. Beke listened intently to Milne's report as he went into great detail describing the events of the day. The expedition had successfully reached the summit of Jebel Baghir but alas it was not the volcano Dr. Beke had hoped it would be.

Milne continued his investigations in the immediate area to find a mountain of volcanic origin but each time he reported his findings to Dr. Beke the end result was always the same - not a volcano. Naturally Beke was disappointed but he did take some comfort in having found Jebel Baghir to be a 'Mountain of Light' — a consideration of Dr. Beke's based on the tempestuous weather that the expedition had to contend with.

The last leg of the expedition required Milne to search for a cave which supposedly signified where the Israelites crossed the sea (as stated in *Exodus*).

Although Milne had not found what he considered to be a cave, in discussion with Dr. Beke, enough had been described to the old man to convince him that there was indeed a cave. Dr. Beke eventually satisfied himself that he had located *his* Mount Sinai even though it proved not to be a volcano. After a ten day journey across the 'Desert of et Tih', they arrived back in Suez on the 15th February. Milne immediately left for England leaving Dr. Beke to report his discoveries to the Khêdive in Cairo.

The findings of Dr. Beke's generated a great deal of controversy in the UK, however, he didn't live long after his return to England to defend his beliefs. It was left to Charles Beke's widow Emily to edit much of her husband's findings, the results of which were eventually published four years later as *'Discoveries of Sinai in Arabia and Midian'*. In the final publication, Emily recognised and paid tribute to the help and support that young Milne had brought to her husband's expedition.

Milne kept his distance from the intense biblical dispute by concentrating on preparation and reading of papers to the Royal Geographical Society. In the meantime he had passed on his collection of fossils found on the Sinai expedition to the British Museum. In 1874 Milne published *Geological Notes from the Neighbourhood of Cairo* in the Geological Magazine and a year later, in the Journal of the Geological Society (QJGS) of London, he published *Geological Notes on the Sinaitic Peninsula unit, North-Western Arabia*.

Across Europe & Asia: an epic journey to Japan

From a quite unexpected source, the next opportunity of employment came from the Meiji government of Japan who offered young Milne a three year contract as Professor of Geology and Mining at the newly formed Imperial College of Engineering in Tokyo. Milne enthusiastically accepted the appointment but this was tempered by how he was going to get there. Not being fond of journeys by sea because of sea-sickness, he decided to travel overland to Japan, although he accepted that he would have to endure a short sea crossing from perhaps Vladivostok to Tokyo. Many of Milne's contemporaries thought that an overland route across Europe, Russia, Siberia, Mongolia and China was too fraught with danger and that he should reconsider the sea route option instead. Milne however saw it as an excellent opportunity to increase his geological knowledge. The route that he chose crossed Asia almost along the line of the present Trans-Siberian railway. The epic journey took 11 months to complete.

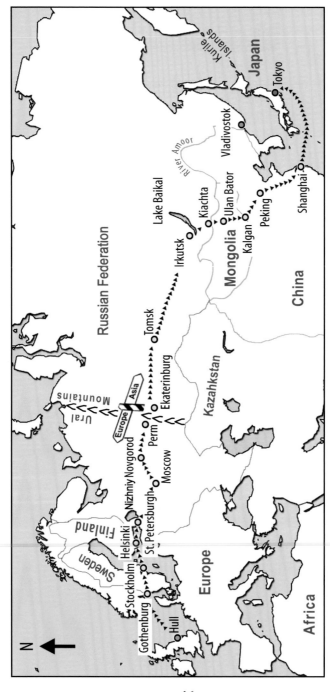

Fig. 11 *The route from Hull to Tokyo (1875–1876). The Amoor (Amur) river (literally "Black River") is the world's eighth longest river. It forms a part of the boundary between Siberia and China, and flows into the Sea of Okhotsk. Adapted and redrawn from John Milne Father of Modern Seismology by L. K. Herbert–Gustar and P.A. Nott (1980).*

John Milne was in his twenty-fifth year, already an experienced traveller, physically fit, a Professor, and ready for the challenges that lay ahead. He advertised in the journal 'The Field' and a number of other newspapers for a travelling companion though without success. Unperturbed he left for Hull on the 3rd August 1875 where he planned to board a passenger ship for Gothenburg in Sweden. His decision to take the even longer Scandinavian route was partly based on the fact that he had friends in Stockholm. He realised right from the outset that difficulties with language would mean valuable information and discussion would be lost. His perseverance and humour in combating this is noted by the following quote: *"My linguistic troubles were overcome by pantomimic representation, an art in which, I found, by practice, I became considerably improved."*

When Milne arrived in Hull, the ship he was travelling on was not what he expected; in fact it turned out to be a coaling steam-boat. He had no intention of allowing this to deter him from his journey, so amidst the clouds of coal dust, he boarded the vessel and set sail. Milne spent two days in Gothenburg exploring the town in general and the geological museum. In one of the museums his attention was drawn to the Swedish elk and the American moose. Contrary to popular opinion at the time, they were not in Milne's view identical. He considered the elk to be noticeably slimmer than the moose.

The rail journey from Gothenburg to Stockholm was pleasant but uneventful and covered about 300 miles (480 kilometres). In addition to visiting as many of Stockholm's museums as time would allow, Milne had to contact the Russian Consulate in order to obtain a visa for his passport.

From Stockholm Milne boarded a steamship bound for Helsingfors (Helsinki), Finland before continuing on to the Russian port of St. Petersburgh. The steamship crossed the Baltic Sea before entering the Gulf of Finland where careful navigation was necessary for successful passage through an archipelago of small islands so characteristic of this part of Scandinavia. Milne once again noticed that snow and ice must have had a profound influence on the lives of local inhabitants of this region. His observations left him in no doubt that ice had moulded and shaped the landscape and that valleys in particular had been formed through the action of coastal ice. Milne based this assumption on the immediate similarities with Newfoundland where he had first suggested that the abrasive properties of coastal ice had a more important part to play in moulding the landscape than an ice sheet or glacier ice. His continued interest in the action of glacier ice on the landscape may have been inspired by the work of the late Louis Agassiz (1807-1873) who was the first person to scientifically propose that the Earth had been subject to a past ice age.

From Helsinki, Milne set sail in an easterly direction along the Gulf of Finland to St. Petersburgh which at that time was the capital city of Russia. During his one week stay in the city, he made a point of visiting the Winter Palace in order to see the Russian Crown Jewels and a collection of precious gemstones the highlight of which was the Orloff diamond at 194¾ carats. However, he was unimpressed with how the collection was displayed and the inadequate lighting in the Winter Palace.

As a geologist, Milne was critical of the site on which the city stood as St. Petersburgh had been built upon marshy ground. Nevertheless he was full of admiration for the many fine buildings such as St. Isaac's Cathedral, where the architectural delights came second place to the types of rock used in its construction. In particular he was impressed by the imposing massive red granite columns and steps at the entrance to the cathedral and the colourful interior columns fashioned from green malachite and blue lapis lazuli.

After another uneventful railway journey from St. Petersburgh to Moscow, Milne looked forward to spending a few days in the city. His search for a travelling companion continued with sympathetic help from Mr. Leslie of the English Consul who advertised in several daily papers on Milne's behalf. Milne had noted that "*In Russia, young ladies have often to make long journeys alone, and where the distances have to be overcome by driving day and night in carriages over rough and lonely roads, it is more necessary that the lady should have a companion.*" There were six applicants, three of whom were young ladies; however none of them proved suitable. Undaunted by the 'quality' of applicants, Milne embarked upon his customary sight-seeing tour of the city beginning with a visit to Red Square where he was particularly attracted to the brightly-coloured spiralling onion domes of St. Basil's Cathedral. His unique description of St. Basil's is a classic example of his Lancastrian sense of humour! "*Has domes like turnips and spires like carrots, it is so peculiar in design, and magnificent in its colours, that, by an agricultural mind, it might aptly be compared to the closely packed contents of some vegetable garden.*" (*Fig. 12*)

Milne departed Moscow by train for Nizhniy Novgorod (known as Gorky from 1932-90) where he only stayed for one day. Still searching for a travelling companion, and as usual unsuccessful, he secured passage on a River Volga steam-boat bound for Perm on a journey which would last 8 days. Although

Fig. 12 St. Basil's Cathedral, Red Square, Moscow, Russia (1988).

not taken with Perm itself, close by is situated a famous Arsenal or Russian Woolwich where he saw the casting of several large steel guns. He also caught a glimpse of what was considered to be the largest steam hammer in the world, the anvil of which was a single casting of 666 tons. Milne thought it quite odd that they were importing coal from Newcastle in England to fire the furnaces at a cost of £5 per ton because he knew that the nearby Ural Mountains contained significant coal deposits. In fact a recent discovery in the district of Solikamsk had revealed a 13 metre (40 feet) thick coal seam.

Incidentally another famous pioneer of modern geology, Sir Roderick Impey Murchison (1792–1871) who was born in the Scottish Highlands, was commissioned by Czar Nicholas I in 1841 to report on the mineral wealth of Russia. As a result of his research work he defined the geological period known as the Permian (290 to 251 million years ago) which he named in honour of the city of Perm where he remains to this day a well known and respected figure.

Fig 13. The town of Nizhniy Tagil in the late nineteenth century.
Credit: V. Kroupnik

During Milne's journey from Perm to Ekaterinburg, the chief point of interest was crossing the Ural Mountains which form the main geographical dividing range between Europe and Asia and therefore a convenient gateway to Siberia. On arrival at Ekaterinburg, population of about 30 000, Milne found favour with the town and decided to stay two or three days so he booked into a hotel. Once fully rested he set off in search of interesting sites worthy of exploration. Of particular interest to Milne was the region's varied mineralisation. In fact Milne made several visits to the gold mines in the village of Berezovski some 10 miles away and a much longer journey of 150 miles (240 kilometres) to the copper, iron, gold and platinum mines of Nizhniy Tagil. The fascinating geology and mineralogy of the region more than made up for the awful weather and poor roads. It took him two weeks to complete his exploration of this mining region before continuing on his epic journey.

For the next section of his journey to Tomsk, Milne had the opportunity of either travelling overland across the Barabinsk steppes or of going by road to Tumen and there joining a steam-boat for a journey along the River Irtysh and River Ob towards East Siberia. Having had sufficient experience of the roads he chose the river route preferring to spend 8 or 10 days in a steamer rather than 5 days being jolted about in a carriage.

Milne became acquainted with a penniless tailor's apprentice called Kaib who offered to do almost anything for Milne if he would only take him as far as Krasnoyarsk where his parents lived. Partly by working on Milne's feelings of compassion and partly by his untiring solicitations, Milne agreed to take him if he would sew on his buttons, pay the fare at post-stations and act generally as servant (with Milne of course providing the money). After travelling through a countryside of corn fields and fir woods, through villages of log huts, altogether very similar to those on the Russian side of the Urals, Milne reached Tumen on the 23rd September, 36 hours after leaving Ekaterinburg. Here he joined a small steam-boat on the River Toufa which is one of the narrow and shallow tributaries of the River Tobol. After running several times into the bushes on the banks and grazing over many shallows, the steamer anchored for the night. There was a total absence of sleeping accommodation and even the saloon was small and crowded with passengers. It proved impossible for Milne to get adequate rest other than that which could be obtained whilst sitting vertically on a wooden bench.

Next morning, Milne reached the Tobol river. Here the passengers were required to change over to a larger steamer which happened to be towing a barge full of convicts. Milne estimated about six hundred to a thousand convicts. Towing the barge proved unwieldy making it a great impediment to the steamers progress. Every day the steamer generally stopped once or twice to take in firewood. At these times the monotony was varied by the sight of one or two log-huts belonging to emigrants or native settlers. They passed very few villages. If they stopped at one there was invariably a rush amongst the male passengers, many of them carrying empty bottles, to see if milk could be procured. The first one or two were generally the lucky individuals who secured the lion's share. Except for these small excursions which sometimes lasted half an hour, everything was extremely tiresome. All that Milne had to look at were low mud-banks capped with a fringe of willow. When the steamer stopped, Milne had the opportunity of making a closer inspection of the convicts. The sides of the barge was made of iron bars which in Milne's view gave it a likeness to a huge birdcage. The inmates, whose only impediments to walking freely about were some iron shackles, clutched the bars with both hands and put as much of their faces through the vertical interstices as the interstices would allow. Milne considered the barge was perhaps more like one of those well filled cages which would have attracted much attention in any zoological collection. It also seemed to Milne that many of them had taken their wives, or else vice versa, the wives being the malefactors had taken the poor husbands. Altogether with the wives and samovars, notwithstanding the iron bars and shackles, they did not appear to be particularly unhappy. The arrangements on board the steamer were very similar to those Milne had experienced on the River Volga. His companions chiefly amused themselves with card playing, a pastime in which the ladies seemed to be particularly successful, having every night a lap-full of paper roubles to count over as the day's proceeds.

The only place of any note at which the steamer stopped was Tobolsk, a large town of 18500 inhabitants built near the junction of the Tobol with the Irtish. Here everything was built of wood. Tobolsk was chiefly interesting from its historical associations, as noted by the monument built to the memory of Yermack who is regarded as the conqueror of Siberia. There was also another monument, a bell, commemorating the folly of Ivan the Terrible.

After joining the River Ob which in places was about three quarters of a mile wide, Milne's progress became slower because the course was now upstream. He observed a number of Ostiacks who contribute a portion of the aboriginal inhabitants of Siberia. The many pebbles on the river bed suggested to Milne that the steamer was crossing alluvial plains which gave rise to the monotonous character of this part of Siberia. Milne considered that the alluvial plains appeared to be the result of deposition of sand and mud from a huge fresh-water lake of glacial origin brought about by the damming up of great Asiatic Rivers which flow into the Arctic ocean by a barrier of ice. Milne reasoned that the ice in the southern portion of these rivers breaks up generally a month before it does near their mouths thus producing annually a barrier of ice obstructing an unusual flow of water. Milne concluded that *"when taken in conjunction with the fact that the northern portion of Siberia appears during recent geological periods to have been rising, I think that sufficient causes are now in action to produce all the phenomena which the Siberian plains present us with."*

After a journey of 8 weeks Milne arrived at Tomsk on the 6th October 1875. Tomsk had a population of about 29500 inhabitants and contained many fine buildings in the form of churches and government offices which led Milne to believe that this was the chief business town in Siberia. However, during the journey to Tomsk he had become acquainted with two distinguished gentlemen, General Smirnoff and Baron Stackelburg, both of whom were keen to continue without interruption to Irkutsk. By invitation Milne joined their party leaving no time to explore the town. Milne even bought a small Tarantass which is a low four-wheeled carriage used in Russia. When snow falls the wheels can be taken off and the body mounted on a sledge.

As far as Krasnoyarsk, for a distance of about 362 miles, Milne journeyed night and day. Every two or three hours when he arrived at a small village the horses were changed. The road was straight and quite flat with the exception of a few insignificant undulations. On either side of the travellers there was usually a strip of cultivated ground but beyond that there were black woods of scrubby spruce and fir. Milne considered that if it was possible to look down upon this main road of Siberia from a great height he would see it like a narrow band of cultivation and log-hut villages running through a wilderness of wood. However, seeing it as he did, gave him the impression that Siberia was a highly cultivated country.

When he and his companions reached Krasnoyarsk, it was unanimously agreed that they should stop for a wash and a sleep. On the evening of their arrival they were kindly invited by the military governor of the town to dine with him. The governor was evidently delighted to have guests visiting the 'oasis of civilization' over which he ruled. Everything that he could think of he did to entertain Milne and his companions; he talked unceasingly, told stories, brought in his pets for them to see. There were amongst others a fox and a pony, all of which were marched round the drawing room; but it was no use as Milnes inclination for sleep was too great to be overcome by these exhibitions. He made every effort to maintain an interest in the evenings events until at last, completely overcome, Milne fell asleep.

Krasnoyarsk, like most Siberian towns had a club and theatre, but the latter, unfortunately for the inhabitants who like all Siberians so far as Milne could see were very passionate about theatre had little opportunity of securing the services of a troupe of actors.

From Krasnoyarsk to Irkutsk (670 miles) the road was very similar to that from Tomsk. At Nizhniy Udinsk, snow fell and greatly impeded Milne's progress. The roads were so slippery that it often happened, both night and day, that he had to get out of his carriage and help the struggling horses in getting up the hills. Whilst going down one slope, one horse was over-run and had to be left on the road side for dead.

Following this eventful leg of their journey, Milne and his companions reached the last station before Irkutsk. A number of General Smirnoff's friends were already there to bid him welcome. Prior to reaching Irkutsk they passed a large church containing the remains of S. Ennocainti (S. Innocent), who is regarded as the chief of the Siberian saints. He was originally a missionary, who in 1721 was sent to China only to be refused admission, so he finally settled in Irkutsk in 1727. After crossing the Angara river by a flying bridge Milne at last arrived in Irkutsk.

It took Milne 8 days to travel 1 039 miles from Tomsk to Irkutsk (not including the 20 hours in Krasnoyarsk). He took great care of his expenses which for this leg of his journey are itemised on page 25. Note that a verst was a Russian unit of length roughly equivalent to 1.0668 kilometres.

Irkutsk is a popular central Siberian town where short summers and long winters are to be expected. Unfortunately for Milne, unfavourable weather conditions conspired to delay him by a month: the winter roads had not yet been formed, the rivers were not sufficiently frozen for the safe passage of sleighs, yet there was sufficient ice to obstruct the passage of ships. Milne had little alternative but to remain in Irkutsk and seek out accommodation. However, hotels proved too expensive so he decided to take private lodgings.

Milne made good use of his time investigating the regional geology and mineralogy. His findings suggested that this part of Siberia was volcanically active and frequently disturbed by earthquakes. He noted that damage to farmland caused by a rise in the water level of Lake Baikal was good evidence for seismic unrest, whilst clues for volcanic activity were easily traced back to local hot springs and mineral waters.

In preference to making a more detailed investigation of the regions seismic and volcanic disturbances, Milne on this occasion, was more intrigued by the various mining techniques used in the extraction of gold from alluvial deposits of the Lena Goldfield in the Lenski district (*Figs. 14 - 17*). Alluvial gold was first discovered in the Irkutsk region in 1843 but it was not until 1868 that the area became an arena of large scale underground mining as a result of the discovery of rich buried (25-60 metres) placer deposits. The initial deposit of gold-bearing sand and gravel had been sealed by glacial and

WEST SIBERIA

	R	K

WEST SIBERIA

From Tomsk to within 30 versts of Krasnoyarsk,
a distance of 523 versts, 3 horses each 1½ kopecks per verst......... 23. 53

EAST SIBERIA

30 versts into Krasnoyarsk, 3 horses at 3 kopecks per verst. 2. 70

Krasnoyarsk to Irkutsk, 1006½ versts at the same rate.................60. 40

Drink money to drivers at 70 stations.. 7. 0

Grease for wheels.. 3. 50

Expenses in Krasnoyarsk... 1. 50

Blacksmith for repairs to carriage.. 2. 0

Food bought on the road, about. 4. 0

Roubles 104. 63

To this, which is about £15 sterling, must be added
the cost of food which Milne took with him, and
the padorojne or order for horses.

interglacial deposits. In the post-glacial period, the rivers cut down through these deposits to form terraces in some valleys as illustrated in *Fig. 15*.

There was time for Milne to reflect on what he had accomplished so far. The long and arduous journey to Irkutsk was complete so it came as quite a surprise to the young Professor when he was advised by his friends and acquaintances he had made in the Eastern Siberian town to return to England and choose an alternative route if he was serious about reaching Japan. In their opinion the distance to Japan and the fact that little trust could be placed in the Mongols was sufficient reason for Milne to turn back. This was not what he expected to hear nevertheless he had absolutely no intention of turning back; in fact he was already considering his options for the next stage of his epic journey. After making several enquiries it came down to two choices: either sail down the River Amoor to the Pacific coastal town of Vladivostok or travel overland to the Russian border town of Kiachata (Kyakhta) which would mean travelling through Mongolia and China in order to reach the Pacific Ocean.

Fig 14 Alluvial gold mining of a shallow buried placer by adits in the Lena Goldfields, near Irkutsk. Credit: Vladimir Kroupnik

The complicated geological and mining conditions caused the introduction of new methods of alluvial mining.

Fig 15 Extensive open cut alluvial gold mining operation from a deeply (25 metres) buried placer in the Lena Goldfields. Credit: Vladimir Kroupnik

Fig 16 Gold miners sluicing for gold - a small alluvial operation typical for the times of gold rushes in the Lena Goldfields. Credit: Vladimir Kroupnik

Fig 17 Water-wheel in the Lena Goldfields used to lift water for further usage in sluicing - a typical installation for many alluvial operations in the Urals and Siberia in the second half of the 20th century. Credit: Vladimir Kroupnik

Milne reluctantly rejected the route following the River Amoor because of the possible threat of more delays due to frozen rivers and ports. The idea of 'hanging around' Vladivostok until April before he could set sail for Japan was something he was keen to avoid so on the 23rd November he left for Kiachta in a sleigh with just a Russian driver for company. His route took him close to Lake Baikal, the largest (by volume), deepest, and oldest freshwater lake in the world. Milne had intended crossing Lake Baikal but the quantity of ice on the lake still prevented steamers from making a safe crossing. Convinced that he had made the right choice, he bypassed Lake Baikal in a south-easterly direction passing through the old volcanic district of Kalenishnaya. The pleasant countryside couldn't disguise the fact that it was a very cold and lonely journey in a region that was known to harbour dangerous escaped convicts. Without enduring further mishaps, his arrival at the Mongolian frontier was greeted by a significant drop in temperature of sufficient severity to begin to freeze his moustache and beard making it difficult to open his mouth. To make matters worse all his food and wine had frozen solid. Milne nevertheless felt satisfied that he had prepared well enough for the journey even though his sheep-skin clothes seemed to offer little protection against the bitter cold.

At Kiachta Milne experienced further delays before he could enter Mongolia. He had planned to link up with the Russian officer he had met in Irkutsk who was on government business, however, officials in Kiachta would not allow them to travel together because it would have constituted a breach of diplomatic regulations. Reluctantly Milne said his goodbyes to his friend and began making preparations for joining a camel caravan that was due to depart within the next few days.

After 11 days in Kiachata he left on the 9th December with four camels and a small two-wheeled Chinese cart called a *Telega* or a *Turga*. He was also granted a Cossack attendant by the local Commissary. To expedite matters, Milne set up a contract with the Mongols to get him to Kalgan (Zhangjiakou) in 30 days for 100 silver roubles. The camel caravan's daily routine was to keep moving until about 7 or 8 pm at which time they would stop at a yourt (a Mongolian felt tent) for refreshments which usually comprised of a cup of tea in Milne's case. Throughout the journey, he continued making notes on all kinds of aspects of the landscape from the types of trees to the sand and granitic rock fragments which formed the thick deposits of alluvium. When the camel caravan arrived at the Makatah Pass the route became more hazardous and cold enough to bridge icicles across his mouth and freeze his beard to his coat. Milne derived encouragement from the fact that the Mongolian capital city Urga (Ulan Bator) was not too far away.

When he reached Ulan Bator (founded in 1639) it became quite apparent to Milne that it was likely to be the religious centre of Mongolia. Churches seemed to dominate the city and frequently made their presence felt by their constant booming noises, which according to Milne, signalled that church services were being held. Many of the 15 000 population lived in small mud houses similar to those he had observed in Arab villages. There was a busy open square with shops that at night were packed up and carried home. He made his way to the Russian Consulate just 1½ miles outside the city where he was warmly greeted. The following day he left Ulan Bator.

The cold weather took some getting used to as afternoon temperatures typically hovered around -14° R (on the Réaumur scale where the freezing point of water is 0 degrees Réaumur) and at night temperatures plummeted to about -25° R. Such low temperatures failed to deter a number of black ravens from accompanying the camel train. Milne considered them quite troublesome because of their frequent attempts to get at the provisions the camels were carrying. At mid-afternoon the daily meal was cooked on a fire made out of camels' dung which Milne considered far more 'offensive' than if they had used horse dung or cow dung. Even in such an inhospitable environment he still continued making his daily geological observations of the landscape noting such features as *"hills of black and reddish rocks of volcanic origin."*

There was little time to spend with the Mongol people although he did note a couple of prominent characteristics that even the most casual observer should be able to notice. The first of these was their light-heartedness which was in contrast to the stolidity of their neighbours, the Chinese. The other attractive feature was their hospitality. To Milne, they were *"a simple-minded quiet pastoral people whose volcanic spirit is no longer dormant, but quite extinct."*

The road to Kalgan followed a small water course. Passage was easy as the water was not a continuous stream. Adjacent to the stream bed Milne noted outcrops of black basaltic rocks, pinkish porphyritic felsite and large boulders of granite. Granitic boulders became more prolific making the terrain difficult to cross, even for the camels. By the 4th January the character of the country reverted back to red sand. At this point, Milne left the caravan and pushed on ahead to Kalgan crossing the last range of mountains which he believed to be mainly composed of greenish porphyry and granite.

The final leg of the journey to Kalgan was a hazardous descent through a steep and rocky pass which eventually led him into a small village called Yamborshaw where he caught his first glimpse of the Great Wall of China. In the village Milne greeted his host who happened to be the chief of the Russian post-office. As usual Milne made time to visit many cultural sites such as local temples and the Great Wall which he admired immensely. He also made a point of familiarising himself with the Chinese way of life.

Milne departed Kalgan along country roads passing numerous Chinese villages and towns with uncountable numbers of inhabitants. He was highly satisfied with the accommodation on offer, quite unlike that which he had to endure in Mongolia. He passed through the famous Nankow Pass where he got another good view of the Great Wall of China. Four days later he arrived in Peking (Beijing) where he met up with the Russian officer who had taken *only* 48 hours to complete the journey from Kiachta to Peking (Milne had taken 5 days). He spent a week in Peking with Dr. Bushell of the English Legation and allowed enough time to view many of Peking's interesting cultural sights.

Now fully rested Milne continued on to Tientsin (Tianjin), a journey which he completed in 2 days. He allowed himself one week in Tientsin to fully prepare for the last leg of his Chinese journey to Shanghai in the company of the Russian officer, Colonel Unterberger. He would probably have preferred the option of crossing the Gulf of Pechelee but this was out of the question because it was still frozen over.

Together they left Tientsin for Shanghai on the 5th February, both with two 2-wheeled Chinese wagons each harnessed with two mules. Milne also took a saddle-horse. On the next day (6th Feb.) Milne arrived at the Grand Canal at a place where it was about 50 yards in wide. The canal was frozen and numerous sledges were being pushed along its smoother parts. From the embankment, which is a local landmark to the surrounding country, Milne obtained good views of the countryside. Everywhere the ground was flat and under cultivation. Its monotony was varied by clumps of houses (each of which had a few trees about it) and by the conical mounds of numerous graves. Foxes and hares seemed to exist in large numbers. The latter were frequently the target of hawks, in particular, the Goshawk and Sparrowhawk. Not long before reaching Tsinze, Milne passed through a breach in the two banks of an old canal, each of which was about 30 ft. in height. It ran east and west and at one time joined the Grand Canal.

On the third day (7th Feb.) Milne passed along the east side of the long embattled wall of Tsang-jow. After half an hour, along the right-hand side of the road, Milne noted the remains of an avenue of images which represented full-sized squatting horses and large white squatting men. The general arrangement of the figures was similar to that of the tombs of the Emperors to the north of Peking. For most of the day a slight breeze from the south-east drove clouds of dust around which proved painful to the eyes. All the villages Milne passed through had much the same appearance. The entrance was generally through a gateway in a mud wall. Streets were narrow, uneven, dirty, and houses had smoothly plastered mud walls.

Early on the following morning (8th Feb.) Milne passed through the city of Tunghow, the walls of which were much decayed. Before midday he climbed an embankment which was either that of the Grand Canal or of some continuation of it. Owing to the dust storms, the ice which covered it was very rough. At the town of Songer, which he passed through in the afternoon, there was a proliferation of trees and temples. Up to now, his journey through China had been dominated by the sight of willow trees but here, Milne was greeted by a few black groves of Arbor vitae (evergreen emerald trees or shrubs of the genus Thuja). At Dajorw, Milne caught a glimpse of the new year festivities in the shape of a large paper dragon about 20 to 30 yards in length accompanied by a band as it was paraded about the streets.

In connection with local festivities, Milne encountered fireworks and dragons in towns and villages for several successive evenings. The Chinese seemed to be fond of pyrotechnic displays even though Milne had been made aware that fires, which might in consequence be expected, were not common. The wind which had been blowing rather freshly on the previous day, slightly increased, and shifted round to the south-west bringing with it dust from the roads and open ploughed land. The sky became like a fog so Milne was compelled to halt much sooner than he anticipated. He observed many travellers along the road most of whom were travelling on foot or in wheelbarrows. If and when the barrows were being propelled with the wind in their favour, the Chinese travellers would hoist a small sail to aid their passage.

On Friday the 11th Milne approached Shantung Province where the sight of hills was a refreshing change to the monotony and dust of the alluvial plains. In the early morning Milne arrived at the banks of the Yellow River and was rowed across in a small cranky barge. The water, which was thickly charged with mud and covered with pieces of floating ice, was at least from three hundred to four hundred yards in width. From watching pieces of ice floating down in mid-stream and timing several of them as Milne walked along the bank, he found that they travelled with the current at the rate of about 200 feet per minute (approximately 60 metres per minute). Milne now noticed along the roadside many Parson Crows and Blue Jays which he had not spotted farther to the north. As he approached the hills, he passed through several natural cuttings in the alluvium which flanked their sides. This alluvium, instead of being a homogeneous mass of consolidated silts like that upon the plains, contained pieces of limestone derived from the hills upon which it was lying.

At a village called Kais-a, the high and rugged hills were formed from a bluish black limestone and for the first time Milne now saw a few sheep and goats. The hills gave way to mountains where he passed through many narrow defiles of alluvium. The villages in the mountains were strikingly different from those on the plains. The entrance to them was through a high and massive gothic archway over which there rose a gable-ended house. These entrances, which were noteworthy from their picturesque appearance, were very similar in the various towns. The houses, instead of being built of mud like those on the plains, were here built of stone and the roofs were thatched. About 8 am on Saturday (12th Feb.) Milne noted that limestone mountains had ended giving way to granite. With the change the roads and the hills on either side became much rougher.

Everywhere there were people on the move from before sunrise until after sunset. There was also a great number of beggars, many of whom were half-clothed and naked children, women and old men; all very dirty and covered in sores. At mid-day just outside Tientsin, Milne caught sight of freshly decapitated heads hanging alongside the road in wickerwork cages. This was not an entirely pleasant experience for Milne and to make matters worse, he was frequently referred to as a 'foreign devil' by the locals and often refused entry to inns. By the afternoon he had passed through Kinnan (Tainan) which nestles at the foot of high rugged granitic mountains. By night-fall Milne forded the River Vanko which was about a 100 yards in wide and deep enough to come up to the axle-trees of his waggon.

The next morning (13th Feb.) Milne passed through countryside that reminded him of mining districts in Cornwall. From material used in building some of the houses and walls, Milne concluded that in addition to granite, which he saw *in situ*, there must also be limestone in the region. The following morning, travelling over weathered limestone in the cart became somewhat unbearable for Milne so he decided to walk. During the next few days the limestone began to outcrop with accompanying beds of sandstone and shale.

The final leg of the journey was on the Grand Canal and the weather conditions were favourable for a rapid progress. On this occasion the high sloping banks on either side of the canal prevented Milne seeing much of the surrounding countryside. Now and again he passed a war-junk carrying a cannon at its bow; he also passed several large forts, some of which were still being constructed.

There were so many Junks along the canal that Milne was able to make a comparison with shipping at the London Docks. Fishermen and beggars were also numerous. Milne was intrigued by the manner in which beggars collected alms from the passing boats — "*They had several long bamboos lashed together forming a pole of great length. At the end of this a small deep bag was attached. In order to lift the immense rod and present the bag to the passengers on the various levels of the passing junks, the whole was supported on the top of a post driven in the shore and turned about upon it like a swivel. The master of the begging machine stood on the shore beating a small drum to attract attention whilst he worked the rod, raising lowering and swinging his bag into any position where he thought a return might be expected.*"

At last, on the 23rd February 1876, Milne arrived in Shanghai after a 19 day journey from Tientsin. Shanghai to Tokyo would have been a straightforward sea voyage which even Milne surely wouldn't have minded, even if he was sea-sick. Weary from his efforts and no less delighted by his achievement, he had done what many of his friends and colleagues in England thought impossible. In his notes the many difficulties he had to overcome were often minimised, instead, he preferred to focus on the interesting geological formations he had seen and the fascinating flora and fauna he had encountered on his epic journey.

Further observations of his epic journey

Professor Milne's experience of his *Journey across Europe and Asia* was published in the Transactions of the Asiatic Society of Japan (Volume 7, pages 1-72). It also contains additional geographical observations documented under the heading of *Observations and General Notes*, in which Milne lists the principal towns in Siberia together with their date of foundation, population, and distance from St. Petersburgh. He also produced meteorological tables describing the number of days of rain and snow in parts of Siberia, a table of mean temperatures, and a table of the time of freezing and breaking up of the ice in various rivers.

Also included is a section on *Siberian Exiles* and a further section on *Notes For Persons Intending To Make The Overland Journey* in which Milne categorically states what the conditions were like and suggests that foreigners allow 70-80 days depending on what season of year they decide to travel with summer or winter being his preferred choice. Winter offers quicker travel times and the ease of carrying large quantities of provisions, which in Milne's view has to be balanced against the exceptional cold and the cumbersome travelling attire. Summer travelling is usually very warm and dusty with many mosquitoes. If the journey is made in winter, then Mongolia is best avoided due to its Arctic-like environment. Given the right circumstances, Milne would have rather taken a steamship down the Amoor River eventually arriving in the coastal Russian city of Vladivostok.

Milne spoke favourably of his fellow travellers. In his experience, he found them to be kind, hospitable and generally good company which helped lessen the cold and uncomfortable parts of his long and winding road. Partly as a consequence of this remarkable journey, Professor John Milne was elected to the Fellowship of the Royal Geographical Society — an honour richly deserved.

Chapter 3

The Land of the Rising Sun

On the 3rd February 1867 at the age of fifteen, Mutsuhito succeeded his father the Emperor Komei. He took the title Meiji, meaning *enlightened rule* and remained Emperor for 45 years until 30th July 1912. This period of Japan's history is commonly referred to as the 'Meiji Restoration of 1868' which brought to an end the 265 year-old feudalistic Tokugawa shogunate.

The Japanese Meiji Government issued a *Five Charter Oath* in 1868 with a view to improving public morale and attracting financial support for the new government. One of the five provisions in the charter was *the international search for knowledge to strengthen the foundations of imperial rule*. On this basis a large number of foreign specialists were invited into the country to train Japanese nationals in the social, political and economic development of their emerging nation. In order to support and accommodate the academics, the government formed the new Imperial College of Engineering in Tokyo in 1873 which for a while was the largest technical college in the world.

Milne was just one of many invited professionals. His contract of employment contained restrictive clauses related to the type of work he would be doing. In Milne's case as a mining engineer he was authorised to deal with only technical matters and was not allowed to invest his money in any of the country's mines whether they were discontinued, operational, or projected. Lending money to Japanese nationals as a means of acquiring investments was also forbidden. A house named 'Yama Guchi' (Mouth of the Mountain) was provided by the government. For Professor Milne it proved an eventful first night in his new home as an earthquake roused him from his bed. The quake did enough to sway his house from side to side and proved a fitting introduction to the country. At this time Milne was unaware that earthquakes and their related effects would one day come to dominate the rest of his working life.

In 1876 when John Milne joined the college staff, the Principal at the time was Henry Dyer (1848-1918), a Scottish Engineer and graduate of

Glasgow University. Fortunately for Milne, his introduction to college life was undoubtedly made easier by the presence of Irishman John Perry (1850-1920), a Professor of Engineering who he had known back in England. In Japan they became close companions and ultimately lifelong friends.

Milne's daily teaching schedule began at 06 00 and ended at 16 00, however, during the hours between 18 00 to 22 00 staff were expected to participate in private study and recreation; they were also expected to correct student scripts, answer queries if any, prepare lectures and assist in the development of new courses. The subjects he taught included mining, architecture, chemistry and metallurgy. As most of the academic staff were British, the courses were delivered in English; this naturally made them more challenging for Japanese students with little or no English language skills. The engineering curriculum was particularly rigorous as it took seven years to complete before the students could be awarded an M.E. (Master of Engineering).

In his time at the Imperial College Professor Milne gained a reputation for thoroughness. When textbooks proved inadequate he compiled his own course notes in order to maintain a high standard of achievement. His notes on crystallography were in fact lithographed and sent to England for publication. The textbook of some seventy pages was eventually published as *Notes on Crystallography and Crystallo-physics* (Trübner & Co.) in 1879. He returned to this topic again in 1880 when he published a lengthy paper entitled *Experiments on Elasticity of Crystals* for the Mineralogical Magazine. Professor Milne worked hard and set high standards at the Imperial College. He was a young energetic man, in his late twenties, with a passion for field work which he exploited to further his knowledge and understanding of Japan's social history, its many active volcanoes and frequent earthquakes.

During 1877 Milne began to take part in important field investigations of Japan's volcanoes. He climbed most of the volcanoes he visited and conducted many experiments, usually in complete disregard for his own safety. Milne's work was nothing less than a full description of each volcano whether active or dormant. The same attention to detail was extended to his published papers which were meticulously illustrated with his own hand drawn sketches. His commitment to volcanological research is highlighted by the ground-breaking exploration of the Kurile Islands which are situated between Hokkaido and the Kamchatka peninsula of the Russian Federation. Of the many active volcanoes visited by Milne, the island volcano of Izu-Ōshima, along with Mt. Asama and Mt. Fuji on Honshū, are three of the most well known in Japan.

Izu-Ōshima (Ōshima Volcano)

About 100 kilometres SSW of Tokyo, Ōshima volcano in Sagami Bay occupies the northernmost of the Izu Islands and is one of the most active volcanoes in Japan. The eruptions usually come from the 4 km caldera which is occupied by a central cone, Mihara Yama. Ōshima is a dominantly basaltic and andesitic stratovolcano which is liable to explosive activity. Whilst Milne was in Japan, Ōshima was active from 27th December 1876 to February 1877. A series of Strombolian eruptions resulted in the formation of a scoria cone (Nauman-oka). The last major eruption began with fire fountaining (Fig 19) out of Mihara Yama on the 15th November 1986 after 12 years of dormancy. On the 21st November fissure eruptions of lava necessitated the evacuation of residents and visitors from the nearby city of Motomachi.

When word reached Milne that Ōshima volcano was erupting, he considered an opportunity of this nature too good to miss. He promptly assembled a small team, booked a steamer, and departed for Ōshima via Yokohama and the Izu Peninsula; a journey that took just over 24 hours to complete. Local inhabitants on the island informed Professor Milne that the volcano had been active for 16 days. Beyond that he gained little from the local people during his preparation for the trek to the summit. The ascent towards the highest peak was hard going because of the black scoriaceous ash which lay underfoot. Eventually, after a long hard climb, Milne arrived at an old steep-sided crater. As

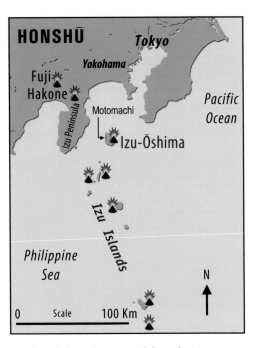

Fig. 18 Location map of the volcanic crater Mihara Yama, Izu Ōshima Island.

they navigated carefully around the rim, a slope of ash was discovered which led to the bottom of the crater. Milne made his descent to the bed of the crater after 'throwing caution to the wind'. Explosions gradually became louder, more frequent and were usually accompanied with shaking of the ground.

Fig. 19 Strombolian eruption of Ōshima in November. 1986. Credit: Shun Nakano

Fig. 20 Air view of the summit crater of Ōshima volcano, 27th September 2000. Credit: Shun Nakano

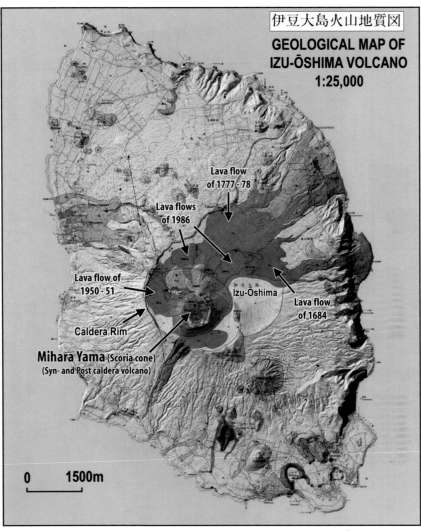

Fig. 21 Original map: Kawanabe, Y. (1998) Geological map of Izu-Ōshima Volcano, Geological map of volcanoes, No. 10, Geological Survey of Japan.

Later they reached the rim of a second crater. What Milne saw was *not* what he expected — "*Instead of looking up at a crater we were looking down into one.*" Milne observed an amphitheatre of rocks about 1 km wide and with walls of about 100 metre tall. In the bottom was a small cone roughly 20 metres in diameter spewing out molten lava. Poor weather conditions and their dangerous proximity to the erupting volcano did not prevent Milne from completing a thorough investigation into the eruption. After weathering the onslaught of cold and rain, descending fine ash and sulphurous odours, Milne retreated back down the mountain and set sail for home the next day.

The geological report of the eruption took Milne one more step towards his understanding of the way in which volcanoes form. He was also aware that volcanic episodes of this nature were supposedly the cause of major earthquakes in Japan. This belief would be thoroughly tested by Milne in time.

Asama Volcano

Located 140 km NW of Tokyo in the Gunma / Nagano Prefecture, Mount Asama (or Asama-yama) is one of Honshū's most active volcanoes. Like Ōshima it is a stratovolcano composed mainly of cinders and ash; the main rock types are andesite and dacite. During Milne's time in Japan, Mount Asama frequently burst into life, beginning in June 1875, with further activity in 1879, 1889, 1890-1892 (sporadic activity) and finally 1894 in which there was considerable ash fall-out. Asama last erupted on the 1ˢᵗ September, 2004 and intermittently continued erupting until the 10ᵗʰ October 2004. Ash reached as far as Tokyo coating everything in a fine dusting of grey ash. The cause of the eruption was apparently due to a build-up of accumulated volcanic gases. This makes detection difficult and therefore Asama continues to be a dangerous volcano.

In the same year that Milne climbed Ōshima he also climbed Mount Asama. However, his time at the summit was brief due to the loud roaring and large volume of sulphurous vapour that was constantly being vented from deep within the crater. This expedition was promptly terminated because even Milne considered Asama too dangerous at the time. Future reports from external sources of the enormous depth of the crater prompted Milne to make a second attempt on Asama but once again the weather intervened and he was beaten back, this time by extremely high winds. Continued conflicting views on the depth of the crater encouraged Milne to make a third attempt to reach the summit of Asama. After a 5½ hour trek from base camp his team reached the summit and were able to conduct a number of experiments. Unfortunately

Fig. 22 *The volcano Mt. Asama from Nakasendo Kutsukake Inns (circa 1891).*
Credit: Nagasaki University Library

Fig. 23 *Mt. Asama. Credit: Kaori Kurita, 20ᵗʰ February, 2002.*

most of them failed. With the aid of copper wire and twine the team did manage to establish that the depth of the crater was at least 230 metres. Milne, again throwing caution to the wind, crawled out onto an overhang in order to catch a glimpse of the crater bottom. This trek to the dangerous Asama volcano was later described by Milne as a 'holiday excursion.' During his 20 years in Japan he climbed more than fifty different volcanoes during the college's long summer holidays. In 1878 he made perhaps his most memorable volcano visit of all — to the largely unknown Kurile Islands.

The Kurile Islands

The Kurile Islands are a chain of mainly unexplored volcanic islands extending roughly 1 200 km (750 miles) from the tip of the Kamchatka Peninsula (Russian Federation) to northern island of Hokkaido, Japan. The formation of the Kurile Archipelago began in the late Cretaceous and to-date there are 68 volcanoes of which 36 of them are considered active and potentially dangerous. In 1875 Japan ceded all of Sakhalin Island to Russia in exchange for the sparsely populated Kurile Islands (18 islands from Shumshu to Urup). The Kuriles were held by Japan until 1945.

Situated at the northern end of Paramushir Island, Ebeko volcano (Fig. 24 and Fig. 25). It is located 7 km to the west-north-west of the main town, Severo-Kurilsk. Ebeko (1 156 metres) is a complicated somma volcano with a central crater filled by a lake about 20 metres deep. Volcanic activity recorded since the late eighteenth century has been restricted to small-to-moderate explosive eruptions from the summit craters. The 2 400 year old volcano last erupted in 2005.

On Simushir Island in the central Kuriles there is a 1 540 metre high snow-capped volcano at the southern most point called Milne Volcano (Fig. 26), named after John Milne. Of the three other volcanoes on Simushir Island, the vent and lava flows of Goryachaya Sopka, which last erupted in 1944, can be seen in Fig. 26 on the SW flank of the snow-capped peak of the Milne Volcano.

Professor Milne's Kurile Island expedition in 1878 was severely hampered by fog making landing on islands a tricky prospect. Nevertheless, he still managed to describe in detail many of the islands in terms of their physical features, flora, fauna, and geology. He even discovered a new volcano on Paramushir Island which he ventured to name Mount Ebeko. Being a modest sort of person he resisted the temptation of naming it after himself, unlike many other Victorian explorers who had a penchant for naming some new discovery after themselves. In Milne's paper, *A cruise among the volcanoes of the*

Fig. 24 Mt. Ebeko, an active volcano on Paramushir Island, the Kurile Islands as viewed from the Pacific Ocean in the east. Credit: Alexander Belousov

Fig. 25 Mt. Ebeko, Paramushir, Kurile Islands, Russian Federation. In April 2005 Ebeko began erupting sulphurous gases and ash particles which entered reservoirs supplying water to the city of Severo-Kurilsk. Credit: Alexander Belousov

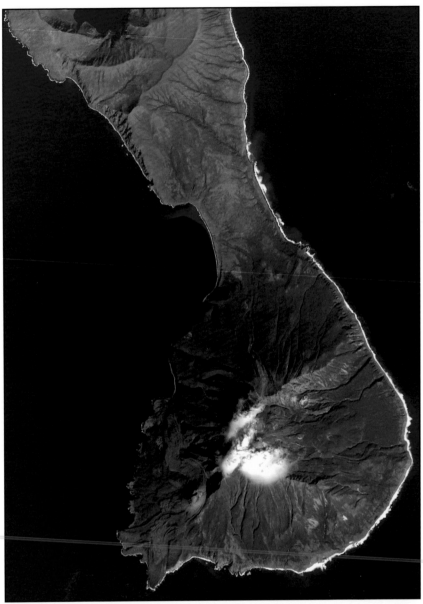

Fig. 26 *Snow-capped Milne volcano on Simushir Island, the Central Kuriles. Vent and lava flows of Goryachaya Sopka are visible SW of the snow-capped peak. Image courtesy of the Image Science & Analysis Laboratory, NASA Johnson Space Centre: (http://eol.jsc. nasa.gov). Mission: STS112 Roll: E Frame: 5671 Mission ID on the Film or image: STS112*

Kurile Islands (1879), he states that "*these volcanic mountains are more recent in origin than those on the Kamchatka Peninsula and Japan since they are less denuded and hold a well-defined form.*"

Milne's comprehensive study of Japanese volcanoes prompted him to conclude that earthquakes were probably not caused by volcanic activity. His exact words were: "*the majority of earthquakes which we experience do not come from volcanoes nor do they seem to have any direct connection with them. In the centre of Japan there are mountainous districts where active volcanoes are numerous, yet the area is singularly free from earthquakes.*"

Today, some of the worlds most heavily congested air corridors pass within a few hundred kilometres of the Kurile Island volcanoes. If a jet airliner inadvertently entered into an ash cloud of an erupting volcano it could severely damage aircraft systems and in the worst case lead to complete engine failure. Ash fallout can also curtail ground operations at airports. Milne would surely have relished the challenge of improving the safety for airline passengers under these circumstances.

During the Kurile expedition Milne met some of the indigenous population known as the Kurilsky. He believed that these people were the only inhabitants of the Kuriles north of the island of Iturup. They had their own language, spoke fluent Russian and also knew something of the Ainu language (the Ainu are believed to be the original inhabitants of Japan). Perhaps this chance meeting with the indigenous Kurilsky was the inspiration for Milne to begin his study of Japan's prehistory.

Prehistory of Japan

Throughout his time in Japan, Professor Milne had many opportunities for travelling through the greater number of its provinces (today known as prefectures). These frequent travel opportunities made it easier for him to further his knowledge of the countries prehistory which at that time during the Meiji era was rooted in gods and spirits that pervaded towns and villages. As luck would have it Milne became interested in Japan's archaeology and anthropology at the time when Professor Morse (1838-1925), also of the Imperial College of Engineering, was actively engaged in the study of the Ōmori shell mounds between Yokohama and Tokyo. Morse reasoned that the remnants of these mounds were probably made by 'savage' pre-Ainu people who practised cannibalism. Professor Milne was eager to contribute to the

Fig. 27 Ainu men in ceremonial costume (c. 1891). Credit: Nagasaki University Library

scientific debate on all aspects of Japan's prehistory; in fact he collaborated with Morse in the exploration of the origins of the Japanese people and in the further advancement of the understanding of the countries archaeology. It was not unusual for western scholars to converge and share experiences with one another; in fact the Meiji government desired such an amalgamation of skills. Together, Milne and Morse completed archaeological excavations in Hakodate and Otaru on Hokkaido which at this time was known as Yezo. As Milne's experience and knowledge of the archaeology of Japan grew, he gradually came to challenge some of Morse's assumptions on the origins of the Japanese people.

Some of Milne's discoveries were published by the Anthropological Institute of Great Britain and Ireland on the 25th May 1880. In his paper on *"The Stone Age of Japan; with notes on recent geological changes which have taken place"* Milne made clear his disagreements with Edward Morse. The paper described and itemised the contents of shell heaps (kitchen middens), tumuli and caves. Common objects that Milne found and identified included sea shells, pottery, bones, arrow-heads and ornaments. His knowledge of geology proved useful when describing axes as noted by the following statement: *"The material of which they are formed is a greenish stone, which in the specimens that I have examined appears to be partly decomposed trachytic porphyry or andesite. From this decomposition hornblende or augite has been partially converted into chlorite, hence the greenish characteristic colour."* He also collected a number of arrowheads made out of either flint or the volcanic rock obsidian. Another artefact found by Milne were the curiously shaped small canine teeth-like stones that were probably used as ornaments in his view. These curiosities were known amongst the Japanese as *Magatama*. Milne noted that *"... these magatama, so far as I am aware, have not been found in shell heaps. They have often been found in the interior of vases which have been dug up. They are made from various materials such as jade, serpentine, jasper, agate, steatite, etc. From these facts, together with the fact that many of them are made of jade, a mineral which I believe as yet unknown in Japan, we must regard the magatama as being an ornament probably derived from China, and certainly historical."*

あさり坂
ASARI ZAKA SLOPE

In 1878 John Milne from the U.K. and Edward Morse from the U.S.A. came to Hakodate, and excavated shell-mounds around this slope with the cooperation of Blakiston, a British resident in Hakodate. In these mounds they found many shells of short-necked clams (asari) which people long ago had eaten. Therefore it was named "Asari Zaka."

Fig. 28 Part of a roadside information column in Hakodate, Hokkaido.

He was satisfied to ascribe the origin of the greater number of relics, more especially those exhumed from the kitchen middens to the Ainu. Milne's accumulated historical evidence on the Ainu is summed up as follows: "*Now the Ainu still inhabit Yezo (Hokkaido), and we know from history that at one time they probably covered Nippon (Japan), and they were driven back towards the north by the Japanese advancing from the south. In fact their history and present geographical position is such that we appear to be safe in assuming that the Ainu have lived for a longer period in Yezo than they have in Nippon.*"

Milne was convinced that the Ainu not only lived in Japan in historic times, but also in prehistoric times. By comparing the markings on pottery with the modern art of the Ainu, and from the general character of the ornamentation, Milne suggested a Polynesian origin be ascribed to the Ainu. Markings on the sheaths of knives and other utensils together with embroidery on their clothes added support to his belief of a southern origin. Today however, current opinion suggests that the Japanese people actually originated from Asia.

In the on-going debate on shell mounds and Ainu origins, Milne was able to draw upon his geological knowledge to help explain archaeological curiosities as noted by the comment on the evolution of the coastline: "... *where heaps of shells like those forming kitchen middens were formed, they must have been near to the sea, just as the modern heaps are; and if we turn to geological evidence, we see that less than 3 000 years ago, heaps like those at Ōmori were in all probability on the seaboard, and that previous to such a period such spots like these, unless we imagine discontinuity in the working of geological agencies, which we see at present, could not have been inhabited because they would have been more or less submerged. Therefore the probability is that these middens were not formed either before or after the time when the place where they exist was inhabited by Ainu. History and geology support each other, and we are brought by them to the same conclusion, namely, that in every probability the kitchen middens of Japan are of Ainu origin.*"

Milne the Seismologist

In 1878 earthquakes in Japan received their first scientific study. I. Hattori, a Japanese official, noted that severe earthquakes had a tendency to cluster. Also a young German geologist, Edmund Naumann, listed Japanese earthquakes and volcanic eruptions in one of his early scientific papers. Naumann was another invited scholar who arrived in Japan aged 20 in 1875 to teach at the Imperial College. During his early years he cooperated and competed with Milne until earthquake studies became Milne's full-time occupation. Naumann is also known to have founded the Geological Survey of Japan.

Professor Milne was absorbed in teaching his students mining and geology, writing up his notes on countries he had visited in the past and completing the manuscript for his first textbook on *Crystallography*. In the meantime, earthquake tremors continued to be a common occurrence and slowly but surely began to attract his attention. He was aware that other British colleagues, particularly William Edward Ayrton (1847-1908) and John Perry (1850-1920), were actively engaged in serious discussion about earth movements in general. Later, when James Alfred Ewing (1855-1935) and Thomas Lomas Gray (1850-1908) took up their posts at the Imperial College, they too were drawn into the earth movement debate. Milne was intrigued and happy to contribute his geological knowledge to the discussions. He in fact commented " *. . we had earthquakes for breakfast, dinner, tea and supper . .*" in his broad Lancastrian accent and entertained the College staff in his own unique way by describing the ancient doctrines and mythology behind earthquakes. He referred to ancient philosophers such as Aristotle (384-322 B.C.) who made an early attempt at a scientific explanation of earthquakes by suggesting that winds that became entrapped in underground caverns caused the earth to tremble when they tried to escape. His theory extended to include steam trying to escape from volcanic vents. Aristotle's theory persisted for nearly two millennia.

Throughout most of human history, natural disasters such as earthquakes were deeply rooted in superstition and mythology. For example, from Kamchatka (Russian Federation) a god named Tuil drove an earth-laden sledge pulled by flea-infested dogs. When the dogs stopped to scratch, the earth shook. From Scandinavia the god Loki was punished for the murder of his brother, Baldur. He was tied to a rock in an underground cave. Above Loki's face a serpent dripped poison which Loki's sister caught in a bowl. From time to time she had to go away to empty the bowl. This allowed the poison to fall on Loki's face. When he twisted and wriggled to avoid the poison it made the ground shake up above him. From Central America, the Mayan Vashakmen are four Gods that support a cube-shaped Earth. They would tip the earth in order to banish the surplus population.

According to Japanese legend, a large catfish capable of supporting the whole Japanese archipelago lives underground. When it shakes itself it causes earth tremors. Following the large Ansei earthquake which struck Edo (Tokyo) in 1855, many varieties of catfish wood blocks or 'Namazu-E' prints were circulated. One particular print tells the story of a captured catfish bearing upon his back high class educated prostitutes. The catfish said to his captors "*I am delighted the beauties clambered on my back. If any more clamber over me I may tremble again.*" Moreover throughout most of human history, different cultures had actively sought magical explanations for earthquakes and other natural disasters. While earthquake legends abound, science eventually provided a simple mechanistic explanation for earth tremors of all kinds.

The journey of the development of an effective seismograph began with Zhang Hêng (78-139), a Chinese philosopher, who is credited with producing the earliest known 'scientific' device (132 A.D.) which could show that a distant earthquake had occurred (although it couldn't actually record the event). The mechanism was straightforward; eight balls were carefully balanced in the mouths of eight dragons placed around the circumference of a vessel. When an earthquake occurred the wave generated would cause one or more of the balls to drop. The idea behind it seems to have been to detect the direction of a distant earthquake so the Emperor's administration could deploy to the correct region reconnaissance teams and emergency response resources.

The dawn of modern seismology surfaced immediately after the Lisbon earthquake of 1755 with the pioneering studies of two Englishmen, John Bevis (1695-1771) and John Michell (1724-1793). However, significant progress in the advancement of earthquake studies began in the mid-nineteenth century with prominent global contributions from the following: De Rossi (1834-1898) and Mercalli (1850-1914) in Italy, Seebach (1839-1880) in Germany, Suess (1831-1914) and Hoernes (1850-1912) in Austria, Montessus (1851-1924) in France and Dutton (1841-1912) in the United States of America. Amongst these distinguished early pioneers I would like to draw your attention to the work of three others, namely, Robert Mallet (1810-1881), Luigi Palmieri (1807-1896) and Filippo Cecchi (1822-1887).

Irish engineer Robert Mallet was a man who Milne admired. He carried out a major scientific field study on the effects of the 1857 Naples Earthquake in which he mapped the earthquake zones around the Mediterranean and produced a contour map showing regions of equal devastation. Mallet believed that earthquakes were caused either by the sudden flexure of part of the earth's crust or by the sharp release of immense forces leading to fracturing of underground formations. He also invented a ground motion detection device (although it wasn't capable of making a permanent record of an earthquake event) and experimented with the use of explosives to generate waves that travelled through the earth in order to time their velocity. This crude technique was devised for his seismographic purpose in 1851 (Milne in later years would continue Mallet's work in this area). Robert Mallet concluded that earthquakes could not be attributed solely to one cause.

In 1874 Italian Luigi Palmieri designed a sensitive three component seismoscope that was able to record unfelt earthquakes. The instrument was brought from Italy for use by Japan's Geographical Surveys Meteorological section. It was operational from 1875 to 1883 before being replaced by a Gray-Milne seismograph. Palmieri's seismoscope (which employed mercury-filled glass tubes) was used to detect earthquakes in Tokyo. The data collected by the seismoscope was catalogued making it a truly functioning instrument of the time (although the device did have its critics). When routine earthquake recording was taken over by the new generation of seismographs developed in Japan, Palmieri's seismoscope, rather than being cast aside, was employed as a triggering device to start recording systems of other seismographs.

The Calabrian earthquake of 1783 had generated a great surge of interest in Italian seismology yet there were few instrumental advances at this time. The Italian Cecchi did however construct an early seismograph and install it in several observatories. Unfortunately the insensitivity of the device discouraged other Italian seismologists from pursuing its development. Historical records show that the earliest seismogram produced from the Cecchi seismograph has been dated 23rd February, 1887. This seismograph had relatively little impact on Italian seismology so the way was clear for the British contingent in the Imperial College of Engineering in Tokyo to develop the seismograph and establish seismology as a new science.

On the cause of earthquakes Milne reiterated that "*the truth was that no-one really knew.*" It didn't take his colleagues long to acknowledge him as their leader as Milne was forthright in his views and clear on aims and objectives. He proclaimed that "*better instrumentation is the key to the problem and the path we should pursue.*" In Milne's view, seismoscopes had limited value and what he wanted was a instrument that could record the motion of the ground during an earthquake, specifically the frequency, amplitude, extent and direction of the waves and exact time it occurred. Progress in his study of seismology was rapid and he quickly acknowledged the imperative need for widespread co-operation. Professor Milne outshone his contemporaries in his dedication in not only inventing a new instrument but in pushing for its world-wide deployment to build up the base of instrumental data. Milne was a true 'workhorse', always looking to extend the boundaries of seismology. His colleagues affectionately referred to him as *Earthquake Milne*.

Seismological Society of Japan

Milne knew precisely what sort of experiments he needed to do and set about influencing colleagues to take an interest and share some of the workload. Also, his professional skills as a geologist and mining engineer enabled him to establish disciplines in the new science. The defining moment when Milne's transition to seismologist occurred was in the early morning of Sunday 22nd February 1880 following an earthquake in the Tokyo / Yokohama area. He described the violent swaying of his house and his difficulty of walking across the floor. From the two experimental long pendulums set up in his house he was able to determine the approximate direction of the shock.

Immediately after this earthquake, Milne, with the assistance of Mr. Toshiwo Nakano, communicated with officials and others in the principal towns of Japan by asking them to furnish information as to the number of shocks they usually felt per year and at the same time, to give as far as they were able, some account of the shocks which had occurred during previous years. From the numerous replies received, one conclusion derived from the analysis of the records was that in Japan there were on average three or four shocks per day (which was the frequency calculated by Professor Heim for the entire earth as noted in Transactions of the Seismological Society, Vol. 4., p. 30). Encouraged by these results, bundles of postcards were sent out to many towns and villages within a distance of about 100 miles from Tokyo, with a request that every week, one of them should be returned with a statement indicating earthquakes which had been felt. The result of these communications showed that nearly all the shocks came from the eastern or north-east seaboard and that very few originated from the west and south-west. Postcard distribution was subsequently extended to a point some 450 miles north of Tokyo.

The results of the survey confirmed to Milne that better seismological instrumentation was the key to making meaningful progress. His next step was to ensure the formation of a society where specialists could share knowledge and work towards a common goal. The society became known as 'The Seismological Society of Japan'. Milne was asked to be President of the new society but declined, suggesting instead that a prominent Japanese official, in this case, Ichizô Hattori (1851-1929) be given the honour.

The Seismological Society met for the first time on Monday, 26ᵗʰ April 1880 in the lecture hall of the Kaisei Gakkō (an amalgamation of various academic faculties renamed Teikoku Daigaku or Imperial University in 1886). Milne was given the honour of delivering the first paper in which he reviewed current knowledge on seismology and suggested areas of future development. He announced a local initiative involving the construction and distribution of 15 seismographs of the pendulum type (as designed by Mr. Gray) be deployed over the plain of Musashi. They were to be installed in telegraph offices so that clocks would be able to record the time at which the shocks are felt. Milne was quick to point out that results from such investigations would be of value not only to geologists but also to builders and engineers. From 1880 onwards Milne's study of earthquakes extended over an interval of about 33 years for which he received grants from the British Association.

The earliest forms of seismographs that Ewing, Gray, Sekiya (1855-1896) and Milne developed were designed around a freely swinging pendulum. In general terms, seismographs operate in the following manner: highly sensitised paper wound around a revolving drum was darkened with smoke black. This forms the chart on which a very fine glass point actuated by the earth tremors scrapes a line on the blackened surface. The more pronounced the wavy line the more powerful the earthquake. This is how the seismograph faithfully records earthquakes no matter where in the world they occur.

Milne's book *Earthquakes and Other Earth Movements* (1886) describes in a more detailed fashion the workings of his seismograph. He writes that "*two mutually rectangular components of the horizontal motion of the earth are recorded on a sheet of smoked paper wound round a drum kept continuously in motion by clockwork by means of two conical pendulum seismographs. The vertical motion is recorded on the same sheet of paper by means of a compensated-spring seismograph. The time of occurrence of an earthquake is determined by causing the circuit of two electromagnets to be closed by the shaking. One of these magnets releases a mechanism, forming part of a time-keeper, which causes the dial of the timepiece to come suddenly forwards on the hands and then move to its original position. The hands are provided with ink-pads which mark their positions on the dial, thus indicating the hour, minute and second when the circuit was closed. The second electromagnet causes a pointer to make a mark on the paper receiving the record of the motion. This mark indicates the part of the earthquake at which the circuit was closed. The duration of the earthquake is estimated from the length of the record on the smoked paper and the rate of motion of the drum. The nature and period of the different movements are obtained from the curves drawn on the paper.*"

The original seismographs installed over the plain of Musashi were greatly modified by Gray, notably by the introduction of a band of paper sufficiently long to take a record for twenty-four hours without repetition. The record was written in ink by means of fine siphons. In this way the instrument, which is extremely sensitive to changes of level, could be made to show that an earthquake had occurred. This was just the first step towards being able to predict earthquakes and how to escape from their dangers.

During the first 12 years of the existence of the Seismological Society, Professor Milne concentrated mainly on localised earthquakes. From 1892-1895 his interests diversified to include distant earthquakes and further experimentation with horizontal pendulums at home and at work. He recognised that the design of the instrument for recording earthquake vibrations had to be simple enough for ordinary people to use. Milne also emphasised that there was a requirement for establishing a vast network of recording stations throughout Japan. The need to be able to determine the magnitude of earthquake waves so that they could be analysed was a critical factor during the experiments.

Although earthquake tremors were common, they were unreliable. For his experiments Milne followed Mallet's lead by simulating earthquake movements by use of dynamite! On one occasion when the dynamite detonated, Milne was caught up in a blast and was lucky to survive the harrowing experience. This somewhat dangerous approach did solve some problems connected with the physical properties of surface earth-motion.

Professor Milne had valuable help in developing the seismograph from two colleagues. Firstly, there was James Ewing who was educated at Edinburgh University and from 1878 was Professor of Mechanical Engineering and Physics at the Imperial University of Tokyo. Besides inventing seismographs, Ewing wrote an exhaustive monograph on *Earthquake Measurement* published in 1883 (Tokyo University Science Department Memoir; 92 pp., 23 plates). Ewing returned to England in 1883 after five years at the University.

Ewing was succeeded by Cargill Gilston Knott (1856-1922) also of Edinburgh University. Knott became Professor of Physics and Engineering in the Imperial University until 1891. His key contribution to the pioneering group of seismologists was to supplement their skills as instrument makers by his own flair for mathematics and data analysis. Knott also introduced geomagnetic surveying to Japan completing a survey of the whole country in only three months. On his return to England, Knott maintained his interest in seismology as noted by the publication of three important papers for the Royal Society of Edinburgh. He studied the behaviour of earthquake vibrations, in particular, the tracing of paths of primary and secondary waves through the earth.

In 1879 Thomas Gray arrived in Tokyo and took up his university post as Professor of Telegraphic Engineering. He was educated at Glasgow University where he studied under Kelvin (1824-1907). Although Gray's residence in Japan was brief (1879-1881) he nevertheless made a significant and highly valued contribution to the development of the seismograph. In fact Milne, Gray and Ewing obtained the first known records of ground motion as a function of time. Furthermore they realised what such records could reveal about the nature of earthquake motion. Their seismographs enabled them to study the propagation of seismic waves and how the ground is affected. The results of their labours were of huge significance to engineers and construction companies. Although seismographs proved effective in Japan, these early varieties were not able to detect earthquakes which occurred in other parts of the world.

Professor Milne was not only deeply indebted to the work and ingenuity of Ewing and Gray, but also of Perry and Ayrton. Unfortunately Milne didn't grasp the importance of damping for seismographs (a damping mechanism helps keep the pendulum steady) which had initially been discussed by Perry and Ayrton back in 1877; their publication on damping was largely neglected. Milne had a close working relationship particularly with Gray and between them they produced the *Gray-Milne Seismograph* (*Fig. 29*). It satisfied all the criteria Milne had stipulated such as being able to record horizontal motion, vertical motion and the time at which the recording was made. Significantly, earthquakes could now be recorded without any attention being required by the observer; this made their distribution throughout Japan a much simpler task. In 1881 Milne took the seismograph to Britain where it was produced by Messrs. White of Glasgow with the cost of production partly being met by the British Association. Gray returned to England in 1881 after only three years in Japan.

The *Gray-Milne Seismograph* was a work in progress and many changes were made in order to improve the resolution and accuracy of the earthquake data being recorded. Milne collected and catalogued as much raw data as he could get his hands on. In his last paper read to the Seismological Society of Japan he presented details of a total of 8 331 earthquakes recorded from 1885 to 1893.

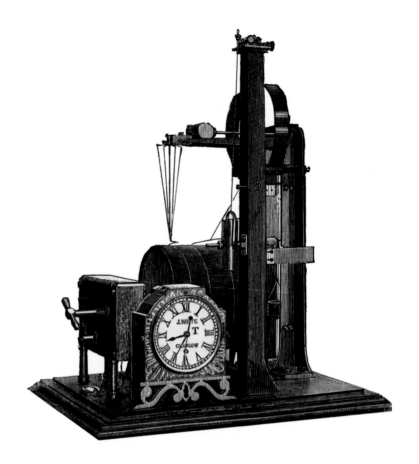

Fig. 29 *Gray-Milne Seismograph (after Milne, 1886). Taken from Earthquakes and other Earth Movements. Kegan Paul, Trench, & Co., Ltd., London.*

As modest as ever Milne described this 'labour of love' in the following way: *"As it stands, it is only a tentative effort to provide investigators with a new kind of data which may lead to investigations not hitherto possible."* His contribution to seismology was recognised back in England when the Geological Society of London awarded Milne the Lyell Medal which was duly accepted on Milne's behalf by Professor J.W. Judd.

The pioneering work Milne was doing in Japan also came to the attention of the Royal Society of London which is one of the oldest and most exclusive societies in the world. As a consequence of his outstanding contribution to science, Professor John Milne F.G.S. was proposed for membership by

William Thompson (Lord Kelvin), Henry Woodward, J. W. Judd, G. H. Darwin, R. Etheridge and John Perry. He was elected to the society on the 9th June 1887 thus becoming Professor John Milne F.R.S. F.G.S. Election to such an eminent body of Fellows must have given him immense satisfaction.

Living in seismic areas where loss of life, injury, and loss of property is an ever present fear, influenced Milne to get involved in discussions on future strategies of designing buildings that could withstand an earthquake shock. He was instrumental in the planning of many new architectural initiatives, for example, piers of bridges were made thicker at the base and were made to taper upwards instead of being built with straight sides as in Europe; brick factory-chimneys were replaced by structures of sheet-iron. The method of building bridges and houses was entirely revolutionized by him.

Milne's work in this area was brought to the attention of the Royal Society of New Zealand by W. M. Maskell's in "*The Late Earthquake (1st September, 1888) and its Bearing on the Architecture of Wellington*". In the paper Maskell states "*Professor Milne, of Japan, probably the highest living authority on the subject, had laid down the following principal rules to be kept in view in building stone or brick buildings in an earthquake country: (1.) So arrange the openings in a wall that for horizontal stresses the wall shall be of equal strength for all sections at right angles. (The meaning of this he took to be that it is better in buildings of several stories not to have the windows all arranged in regular vertical lines.) (2.) Avoid heavy-topped roofs and chimneys. (3.) Let archways curve into their abutments ('archways' here seeming to include window-openings). (4.) Place lintels over flat arches of brick or stone. (Seemingly, Professor Milne's suggestion was that these lintels should be of iron or timber.). Professor Milne also suggested that 'to build high houses would be to erect structures for the first earthquake to make sport of.'*"

His Excellency Arinori Mori, the Minister of Education (1888), invited Milne to advise on building regulations which he duly did with his usual practical and common sense approach. Milne made the point to the committee that the extensive use of timber in buildings increased the risk of fire, especially after an earthquake and that the use of bricks and mortar, despite their weight, was a good means of adding strength to buildings. Some of the ideas put forward by Milne were incorporated into Japanese building regulations.

Other curious aspects of seismic phenomena such as '*earthquakes and magnetic disturbances*' and '*emotional and moral effects of earthquakes*' were also scrutinised by Milne. Another strange phenomena that Milne considered was '*warnings furnished by animals'* as noted by this example: " . . . *before the catastrophe of 1812, at Caracas, a Spanish stallion broke out from its stable and escaped to the highlands, which was regarded as the result of the prescience of a coming calamity. Before the disturbances of 1822 and 1835, which shook Chile, immense flocks of sea birds flew inland, as if they had been alarmed by the commencement of some sub oceanic disturbance.*" Nothing escaped his attention.

For his humanitarian contribution, Milne was decorated by the Emperor with the *Order of Merit with the Cordon of the Sacred Treasure* in 1888. Shortly after this he was granted status of *Chokunin* (a senior administrative position granted through letter of appointment bearing the signatures of both the Emperor and the Prime Minister but without a palace ceremony).

The Mino-Owari Earthquake of 1891

The provinces of Mino (most of the southern part of the present day Gifu prefecture) and Owari (the western half of present day Aichi prefecture) lie approximately 208 km (130 miles) west of Tokyo. The area is occupied by an extensive plain which at the time was covered by a network of rivers and canals and was also one of the chief rice growing districts of Japan. It is in these provinces that the greatest earthquake occurred during Milne's residence in Japan — the first daishinsai (great earthquake disaster) of the Meiji era. The earthquake struck without warning at 06 37 on the 28th October, 1891. Known as the Mino-Owari or Nobi earthquake (Magnitude 8.0), it caused heavy damage to the Gifu and Aichi prefectures. Death and destruction on this scale had not been seen in Japan since the 1855 Ansei-Edo earthquake which destroyed Edo (Tokyo). The complicated nature and effects of the earthquake attracted the attention of a team of seismologists' comprising of Professors' Bunjiro Kotō (1856-1935), Fusakichi Ōmori (1868-1923), Milne and Seikei Sekiya amongst others. Kotō, who was a geologist, undertook a detailed study of the spectacular fault-scarp (*Fig 30, 34 and 36*); Ōmori's task was to monitor the aftershocks; Milne made available data from his catalogue of Japanese earthquakes for the years 1885 to 1892. Kotō, Ōmori and Milne realised the significance of fault movement as being the cause of this earthquake.

Milne was also asked to produce a permanent visual record of the effects of the devastating earthquake. Together with Scottish engineer William Kinninmond Burton (1856-1899) who was Professor of Sanitary Engineering at Tokyo University, they compiled the much sought after publication *The Great Earthquake of Japan 1891* which comprises of 69 pages and incorporates

Fig. 30 Neodani Fault Scarp at Midori, near Gifu (circa 1891).
Credit: Nagasaki University Library

Fig. 31 Iron railway bridge across the Nagara River after the 1891 earthquake. The
bridge was completed in January 1888 by the British engineer C.A.W. Pownall. Three
out of five sections collapsed. Credit: Nagasaki University Library

Fig. 32 Kitagatamachi in Gifuken flattened by the earthquake (circa 1891).
Credit: Nagasaki University Library

Fig. 33 Earthquake damage in Wakamori village in Ogaki (circa 1891).
Credit: Nagasaki University Library

Fig. 34 *Neodani Fault Scarp (2005) is the small slope below centre in the photograph*
Credit: Yutaka Honda.

30 pages of high quality illustrations which made it the most artistic album ever published on earthquake effects on buildings, ground, and seismic scenery. Ken Ogawa, a noted Japanese photographer and collotype printer, contributed in the preparation of the plates. The photographs documented clearly, the failure of western architects and engineers. Sekiya and Ōmori (and Milne) had in fact been critical of western designs. The new crop of Japanese seismologists, which included Sekiya and Ōmori, inherited the responsibility of adapting foreign infrastructure to the peculiarities of their own landscape.

The alluvial Nobi Plain, 'the garden of Japan', was among the most productive and densely populated rural districts in the country and lay astride the highways, railroads, telegraph lines, and other infrastructure linking Tokyo with points south. The road connecting Nagoya with Gifu (the provincial capital) is about 20 miles in length and bordered by many villages. In the aftermath of the earthquake all the villages had been reduced to rubble. *"In some streets," commented Milne, "it appeared as if the houses had been pushed down from the end, and they had fallen like a row of cards."* To make matters worse, fires raged through Gifu, Ogaki, Kasamatsu and other towns. Official returns indicate that 7 279 people died, 142 177 houses were destroyed with a further 80 184 being damaged by the earthquake.

The Neodani Fault that Milne and Kotō investigated is located in the Neo Valley near the village of Midori. Based on the geological investigations of

Kotō, the precise link between earthquakes and faults was finally established. In his report Kotō stated that *"the sudden elevations, depressions, or lateral shiftings of large tracts of country that take place at the time of destructive earthquakes are usually considered as the effects rather than the cause of subterranean commotion; but in my opinion it can be confidently asserted that the sudden formation of the 'great fault of Neo' was the actual cause of the great earthquake."* This was the first time that the cause of earthquakes had been directly linked to the formation of fault scarps. More recent research suggests that during the Mino-Owari earthquake many faults ruptured on the complex Nobi Fault System with the most dramatic displacement occurring along the Neodani Fault. Here, the fault generated its greatest vertical displacements. Left-lateral offsets of as much as 8 m (26 ft.) and vertical offset up to 6 m (20 ft.) were recorded along more than 70 km (44 miles) of fault rupture.

There is a pyramid-shaped Earthquake Fault Observation Museum (*Fig. 35*) in Midori which preserves a trench across the Neodani Fault (*Fig. 36*) spectacularly displaying the 6 metres of vertical offset. In 1952 this fault was designated a National Monument of Special Interest in Japan.

Following the earthquake, Ōmori collaborated with Milne in conducting a survey of the falling or fracturing of stone lanterns and other objects. This led to important experiments between 1893 and 1910 to simulate the behaviour of objects in actual earthquakes by means of artificially 'shaking tables'. Their shaking table experiments were just the first step towards the development of modern day simulators which rely on computer technology to control electro-hydraulic drive apparatus used to induce synthetic earthquakes.

Fig. 35 Earthquake Fault Observation Museum (Jishin Danso Kansatsukan), Midori. Credit: Yutaka Honda

Fig. 36 *Neodani Fault trench inside the Earthquake Museum, Midori showing 6 metres of vertical displacement that occurred. Credit: Nolan C. Evangelista*

The 23 year old Meiji government nation building project had established a thin infrastructure of railroads, iron bridges, telegraph lines, brick factories, and masonry post-offices in the affected region. How 'shocking' then, that the first reports of the earthquake in the Japanese press emphasized the dramatic failure of these 'western-style' structures. The ramifications of the Mino-Owari earthquake disaster in Tokyo captured the attention of the Emperor who ordered the immediate creation of the Imperial Earthquake Investigation Committee *(Shinsai-Yobō-Chōsa-Kwai)* which was orchestrated by Dairoku Kikuchi (1855-1917). Serving members were drawn from many academic disciplines such as seismology, geology, mathematics, physics, architecture and engineering. The main goals for the new committee were to develop methods for predicting earthquake occurrences and for mitigating the earthquake disaster. Suitability of building materials and the methods of construction also became an important consideration. Milne was the *only* foreigner to serve on the committee. As for the Seismological Society of Japan, it was reluctantly disbanded. For 12 years it had served the Meiji government well. Sixteen volumes of Transactions were published in which Milne wrote almost two thirds. The Transactions were succeeded by the Seismological Journal of Japan which Milne continued to edit until 1895 when he left Japan. Seismology in Japan was now fully embraced by well-trained Japanese seismologists. On the death of Seikei Sekiya in 1896, the first professor of seismology in the Imperial University, Fusakichi Ōmori succeeded to his chair and also became secretary of the Imperial Earthquake Investigation Committee. Milne's former student made particularly important contributions to seismology during the next 10 years and became the natural leader in all Japanese investigations on volcanoes and earthquakes writing many important papers in both Japanese and English. He produced the Ōmori horizontal pendulum seismograph and propounded the first version of today's seismic gap hypothesis amongst other valuable works.

Mount Fuji

Mount Fuji, also called Fuji-yama or Fuji-san, is the number one landmark of Japan. Located near the Pacific coast in Yamanashi and Shizuoka and a 100 km west of Tokyo, it is Japan's highest volcano at 3776 metres (12388 feet). It is geologically a very young active stratovolcano. The dominant rock type is basalt although andesite lies at the core. Extensive lava flows to the north helped to create five lakes that make for popular tourist destinations. Initially the volcano was thought to have been created by three eruptions, however, a three-year drilling project that ended in February 2004 revealed evidence of an older eruption. No

Fig. 37 Distant view of Mt. Fuji from the former Kawai village (circa 1891). (Now part of the present Shizuoka City). Credit: Nagasaki University Library

eruptions have been recorded in the 300 years since the Hoei event of 1707. Japan devotes significant resources in monitoring the activity of Mt. Fuji.

Milne had always been captivated by volcanoes — none more so than with Mt. Fuji which dominates the region south-west of Tokyo. He was a frequent visitor and on one occasion spent five days and nights on its summit. Unlike most foreigners Milne had a special reverence for the mountain in much the same way that the Japanese people themselves have. Mt. Fuji perhaps inspired Milne and his friend the Scottish engineer William Burton collaborated one more time to produce *The Volcanoes of Japan, Part 1, Fujisan*, circa 1892. The publication contains 32 pages including 10 black and white plates prepared by Ken Ogawa.

Volcanic eruptions and Earthquakes

The relationship, if any, between volcanic eruptions and seismic events intrigued Milne. He was fairly certain that these two phenomena were connected because they usually occurred in the same region and they shared a common cause; both were a product of some great internal convulsion.

In discussion with Dr. Naumann who had examined the records of the large earthquakes and volcanic eruptions that had taken place in Japan during the last 2 000 years, Milne realised that there seemed to be an approximate coincidence between the times of the occurrence of these phenomena. This led Milne to the conclusion that the efforts which had been sufficient to establish the volcano had at the same time been sufficient to shake the ground. (As previously alluded to, a good example of the synchronisation of these two phenomena is given by Professor Ōmori's classic account of the 12th January 1914 earthquake at Sakurajima (Magnitude 7.1) which was accompanied by large eruptions on Sakurajima Volcano on the southern island of Kyūshū.)

Milne was also aware that there were many examples demonstrating no synchronisation between earthquakes and volcanic eruptions. In Japan, he referred to the 1881 eruption of Natustake volcano a 100 miles north of Tokyo in which there was neither an increase nor decrease in the earthquakes felt in Tokyo. He drew a parallel with the state of seismic activity of 1876-1877 when Ōshima was in eruption. To confound matters he was also able to describe earthquakes and volcanic eruptions which demonstrated some synchronism when he referred to the work of Fuchs, who on the 6th October 1737, reported that the whole of Kamchatka and the Kurile Islands were disturbed by movements which were simultaneous with the eruption of the Klyuchevskaya volcano — one of the highest active volcanoes of the Kamchatka Peninsula. Based on observation and analysis of historic records, Milne concluded that the two phenomena are without any direct connection, unless it was that both are different effects of a common cause.

One aspect he did allude to was that volcanoes may be regarded as 'safety valves of the earth's crust' because of the way in which they provide relief to internal stresses therefore guarding us against earthquakes. Milne's ideas were based on global phenomena (Hawaii, Sandwich Islands, Lisbon and Herculaneum amongst others) and not just events which had occurred in Japan.

Earthquake Catalogues

Above all, Milne was a man of observation and experiments and his seismological works are scattered through a great number of papers and memoirs. Underpinning his work is the value he attached to facts as opposed to theoretical generalisations that are so often disregarded and in time may fade away. But the facts of observation remain. Classic factual-based works by Milne are the numerous earthquake catalogues that he has prepared both for Japan and for other parts of the world. They offer a solid foundation for statistical investigations of all kinds. In his catalogue *"On 387 earthquakes observed during two years in northern Japan" (Transactions of the Seismological Society of Japan, 1884)*, he represented graphically on maps of Japan the areas of disturbance which in this case tended to congregate along the eastern sea board and beneath the sea. Milne was also aware that other seismological organizations neglected this affinity to the maritime origin of earthquakes.

A considerable work was published by Milne in 1895 in which he was able to depict a relationship between seismicity and terrestrial relief. This publication - *"A catalogue of 8 831 earthquakes recorded in Japan between 1885 and 1892"* - was published in both the Transactions of the Seismological Society of Japan (in the year that it terminated) and the Seismological Journal of Japan. A global catalogue was published by Milne in 1911 - *"A catalogue of destructive earthquakes, AD 7 to AD 1899."* Its value was compromised by the fact that Milne did not give the details and the original sources for each seismic event reported. The classification of these destructive earthquakes was made based on Milne's own three degrees of increasing intensity scale. Scale I represented the least destructive being typified by cracking of walls and the breaking of chimneys. Scale II was indicated by the removal of roofs from buildings and or landslip; finally Scale III, the most destructive, is marked by the general devastation of towns and districts; land slips would be more common and the ground may be fissured and faulted. (The first earthquake intensity scale devised was the ten degree Rossi-Forel scale in 1873. This was later revised and improved by Italian volcanologist Giuseppe Mercalli in 1883 and 1902.)

'Windows' of Opportunity

When Professor Milne took a holiday, he invariably spent the time exploring other earthquake-prone regions around the Pacific coastline from the Kuriles to Borneo, the Australian Colonies, the United States, and many other volcanic islands. He was by now becoming more interested in recording distant earthquakes beyond those that were specific to Japan. Previously in 1883 Milne had stated *"It is not unlikely that every large earthquake might, with proper instrumental appliances, be recorded at any point on the surface of the globe."* This notion was Milne's first step towards achieving a global network of seismograph stations and would be vigorously pursued on his return to England.

As you may recall, Milne visited Hokkaido in 1878 to perform archaeological investigations involving the origins of the Japanese people. He also completed a mineralogical survey in which he discovered coal deposits that proved to be the largest in Japan. Milne's working base was usually Hakodate. It is here that he met Thomas Wright Blakiston (1832-1891), a fellow explorer and naturalist from Hampshire, England; they became good friends. Blakiston noticed that animals on Hokkaido had more in common with northern Asian species whereas those on Honshū had affinities to southern Asia. The Tsugaru Strait, which is the natural channel separating Honshū and Hokkaido, marks the major zoogeographical boundary between the two islands. This boundary became known as the 'Blakiston Line', a name in fact apparently suggested by John Milne. Blakiston was a particularly keen amateur ornithologist who laid the foundation for all future work in Japanese ornithology. Like Milne he did not pursue his studies for the glory they might bring him, but in order to satisfy his thirst for knowledge.

Blakiston had been in Japan much longer than Milne and was able to help him improve his knowledge of Japanese etiquette and his Japanese language skills so that he could become less dependant on the services of an interpreter. He also introduced Milne to Jokyo Horikawa, the Abbot of the Hakodate Temple of Ganjo-ji and more importantly to the Abbot's daughter Toné Horikawa who Milne later married in Tokyo in 1881.

Early in 1895, the Milne family suffered a serious setback to their plans. On 17th February their house and observatory was completely gutted by fire. Books, instruments, Transactions of the Seismological Society and occasional publications relating to earthquakes and volcanoes were all destroyed and the cause of the fire was never established. This was probably the defining moment when Professor John Milne decided to return to England. In June, Milne's resignation was accepted by the University. Prior to setting sail for England, John and Toné were married *again* on the 12th June 1895 at the British Consulate; this time according to British Law. Towards the end of the month, Milne attended an audience with the Emperor; in fact His Imperial Majesty commanded Milne's presence. After Milne had returned to England, he was informed that Emperor Mutsuhito had conferred upon him, as a token of His Majesty's appreciation of the value of Professor Milne's services in the cause of science during his long residence in Japan, the rarely awarded distinction of *Third Grade of the Order of the Rising Sun* and a life pension of 1000 yen.

Chapter 4

The Isle of Wight

Whilst Milne was teaching in Japan in 1880, he had persuaded the British Association for the Advancement of Science (BAAS) to appoint a committee *"for the purpose of investigating the earthquake phenomena of Japan."* This committee initially comprised of two people: A.C. Ramsay and John Milne (as Secretary) and their reports began to appear in the BAAS Reports (1882). However, in 1891, the BAAS appointed a committee to investigate earthquake tremors that occur in the British Isles. Charles Davison (1858-1940) and John Milne were appointed as joint secretaries.

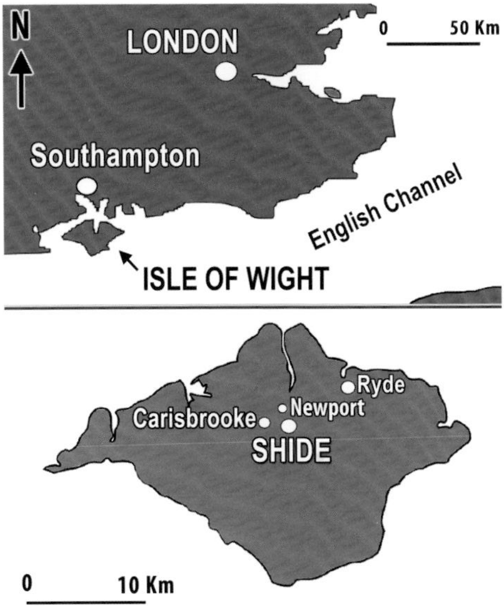

Fig. 38 Location of the Isle of Wight.

Professor John Milne and his wife Toné arrived back in England in July 1895. They began looking for a house with sufficient grounds and the right kind of geological foundation on which a seismograph observatory could be erected. Milne turned his attention to the Isle of Wight and found the ideal setting at Shide Hill House, Shide, near Newport after consultation with Professor J. W. Judd, F.R.S. who was Chairman of the BAAS Committee.

Detailed specific requirements for installation of Milne seismographs were described in his first report to the *BAAS Seismological Investigations Committee* in 1896. He stated that *"the position of Shide Hill House, where instrument (T) is installed, is approximately 50° North Lat., and 1° West Long. It is near to the Shide railway station at the foot of Pan Down, which is a portion of the chalk backbone of the Isle of Wight. Up on*

Fig. 39 John and Toné Milne by the steps to Shide Hill House.
Credit: Seismological Society of America. Taken from 'John Milne, Seismologist'
by Mrs. Lou Henry Hoover

Fig. 40 Seismographs inside Shide observatory. Credit: Patrick Nott

the Down the chalk reaches within a few inches (cm's) of the surface. At Shide Hill House, disintegrated chalk, which may have a thickness of 6 feet (2 metres), is met with at a depth of 3 feet (1 metre). In front of the house or towards the west, at a distance of about 150 yards (approx. 150 metres) at the other side of a small stream, there is a railway. In a NE direction, at a distance of 242 yards, there is a chalk quarry, where at certain fixed times blasting takes place. At the back of the house within a few yards of the buildings in which instrument (T) is placed there is a lane down which on week days carts heavily laden with gravel pass."

Through the kindness of Mr. A. Harbottle Estuourt, Deputy Governor of the island, Milne was able to establish a second instrument (U) within the grounds of Carisbrooke Castle (1¼ miles from Shide) which had been built upon a similar geological foundation to that of Shide. Within a year Milne had installed two seismographs. The monitoring and further development of

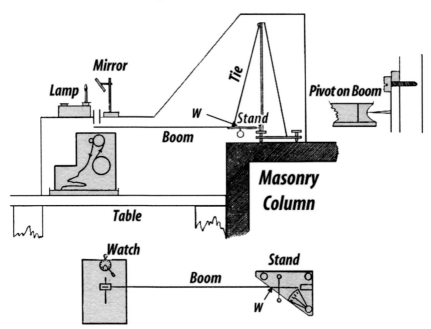

Fig. 41 *Main components of a Milne Seismograph (after Milne, 1898).*
Taken from Seismology. Kegan Paul, Trench, Trübner & Co. Ltd., London.

Light from the Lamp is reflected by the Mirror through the intersection of two crossed slits onto photographic paper. The lower illustration is a top view of the instrument with its outer case removed. A flexible wire (Tie) is holding up the boom. The weight W is pivoted on the boom.

his seismographs was greatly assisted by his friend Shinobu 'Snowy' Hirota who had accompanied Milne from Japan. The Shide observatory itself was to grow both in size and importance during the next few years. In 1900, with financial help from fellow seismologist Matthew H. Gray, an experimental laboratory was constructed. With his Shide observatory now fully established the serious work could begin.

Professor Milne concentrated on the study of unfelt earth movements, both microseisms (small motions in the earth unrelated to earthquakes) and teleseisms (ground motions caused by very distant earthquakes). He made extensive use of a horizontal-pendulum seismograph which he designed in 1894 while still in Tokyo. In due course, more and more of Milne's horizontal pendulum seismographs were installed in both British and Foreign

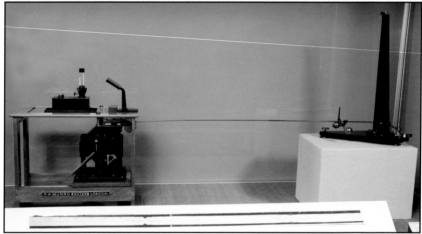

Fig. 42 *Milne Horizontal Pendulum Seismograph, 1899*
This example, made by R W Munro, is number 24 in the series and incorporated several improvements. It was adopted as a standard observatory seismograph by the British Association for the Advancement of Science. Credit: Science Museum, London

observatories. All the recordings, whether registered in the UK or abroad, were sent to Shide for cataloguing and analysis. The Milne seismographs were continually undergoing modification and improvement and thus required his constant attention. In addition, increasing amounts of seismic data was constantly arriving at Shide, so having Hirota alongside to share the workload was of great value to Milne. This kind of support helped Milne to maintain his commitment to the role as secretary to the newly formed BAAS Seismological Investigations Committee.

Having already published a multitude of scientific papers in a variety of journals, Milne now turned his attention to writing two books as part of the International Scientific Series: *Earthquakes and other earth movements* (1886) published by Kegan Paul, Trench, & Co. was followed by *Seismology* (1898) published by Kegan Paul, Trench, Trübner & Co. Another fascinating little book published in Japan by Milne (reprinted in London in 1902) was *The Miner's Handbook* (1893). The book was favourably reviewed in the magazine Nature — "*During his long stay in Japan Professor Milne seems to have acquired the deftness of a native in packing, for it is difficult to conceive how more could have been crammed into a book no bigger than a cigar case and weighing only 6½ oz (1 ounce ≈ 28 grams). It is a veritable miniature compendium of mining which is likely to find its place not only on shelves but also in the luggage of most mining engineers.*"

Great Sea-Waves: the Meiji Sanriku Tsunami

On the 15th June 1896 the north-eastern seaboard of Japan was devastated by a huge tsunami (literally harbour-wave) in which 26 360 lives were lost. The under-sea earthquake which caused the tsunami occurred off the coast near the city of Sanriku. The magnitude of the earthquake measured 7.2 (although 8½ has been quoted elsewhere). To the south of the devastated region, nestling amongst sand-dunes and crooked pines, is the village of Kamakura, which in ancient times was a Shogan's home and capital of the empire with a population estimated at a million. Here the giant wave reached a staggering height of approximately 25 metres (80 feet) before crashing into a religious festival that was taking place on the beach. Milne eloquently stated that "*All that remains to attest to the former glory of this ancient capital is the huge bronze Buddha, so well known to all who sojourn in Japan, which yet sits upon its massive pedestal and with its calm eyes of gold looks out upon the broad Pacific, the home of the sea-god which, has so often created devastation round its feet.*" I. Hattori supervised the recovery from the devastating tsunami which ultimately served as an impetus for tsunami research in Japan.

Milne had been at Shide Hill House for a year when this catastrophe took place. Following the Sanriku tsunami, he immediately turned his attention to this devastating phenomenon which he had not been able to directly investigate during his time in Japan. Milne collected and analysed the data on this mega seismic event before reporting his findings to the BAAS Seismological Committee. In his report he stated that "*The sea-waves which at about 8 pm on 15th June, 1896, invaded the north-eastern coast of Nippon were as destructive*

Fig. 43 *"Daibutsu" (Great bronze Buddha) of Kamakura, Kanagawa Prefecture (circa 1891). Credit: Nagasaki University Library.*

to life as those which accompanied the well-known eruption on 26ᵗʰ August, 1883, of Krakatoa, whilst one of the shocks by which they were preceded *was of such severity that it was clearly recorded in Europe, and in every probability caused a disturbance over the entire surface of the globe. The magnitude of this disturbance,* and the sub-oceanic changes by which it was probably accompanied, make it well worthy of record." Milne suggested that a possible cause may be attributed to the uplift of the Yezo (Hokkaido) anticline and growth of a submarine range of mountains. The significance of this event, as destructive as it was, focused Milne's mind on sub-oceanic changes. His findings were read to and published by the Royal Geographical Society in 1897. Before Milne read the paper, Admiral Sir W. J. L. Wharton, Vice President, commented "Mr. Milne requires no introduction from me, for he has read papers here before, and he has a very important communication to make to us tonight, which I will now ask him to read." This was one of Milne's most thought provoking papers and generated a great deal of discussion at the meeting particularly from Sir Archibald Geikie, Professor John Perry, Matthew Gray and Mr. R. Gray.

Milne's paper on *Sub-Oceanic Changes*, fully explored the implications for global communication by undersea cables. Breakages in cables cost the transatlantic cable companies a great deal of money. Those companies valued Milne's research work particularly in relation to the possible location of faults that could cause cable breaks. The key points of Milne's paper are as follows: "*Beneath seas and oceans there are a certain class of geological changes in operation which are more frequent, and often more intense, than corresponding changes on land. The sites of these changes are to be found below low-water mark at comparatively shallow depths on submerged plateaus surrounding continents and islands, and on the face, and especially near to the base of the steeper slopes of continental domes, and around submarine banks at depths which may even reach 4000 fathoms. On the level floor of oceans, where sediments accumulate with immeasurable slowness, and where for years and years ocean cables lie undisturbed, geological changes are, so far as a lifetime is concerned, not recognisable.*

The submarine operations to which it is particularly desired to draw attention are those which are seismic and volcanic, the former at least often being accompanied by the displacement as a landslide of such enormous volumes of material that the whole surface of an ocean may be agitated. Evidences that such displacements have had a reality is to be found in the conditions under which cables have been buried, and in the marked change in soundings near to spots where seismic efforts have been exerted. Other causes leading to displacement of materials on the face and near to the base of submerged slopes are overloading by sedimentation, erosion, the escape of water from submarine springs, and the effects of currents."

Later on in the paper Milne gives more detail on cable fracture: "*The fact that, on the level plains of ocean beds, cables lie for years and years without disturbance is another testimony to the facts brought together by geologists to show that the flat plains of ocean beds are regions where there is but little change. Directly, however, we approach sub-oceanic banks or the margins of continental slopes, although the depths may be abyssal, the fact that cables after interruption have to be broken away from beneath materials which hold them fast, indicates that regions of dislocation have been reached, and what is true for these great depths is also true for localities nearer land.*

Sometimes cables are bent and twisted, sometimes they are crushed. Now and again sections are recovered which, from the growth of shells and coral on all sides, show that they have been suspended. Others show that fracture has apparently been the result of abrasions; whilst the ends of wires, one of which is concave and the other convex, slightly drawn out, indicate that yielding has been the result of tension. Needle-pointed ends suggest electrolytic action; but, although cable-interruption may occur in these and other ways, the explanation which best accords with the observations made during cable-recovery generally are those which attribute their dislocation to sudden displacement of the bed in which-they are laid, or to their burial by the sliding down of materials from some neighbouring slope. Sometimes it will be seen that earthquake movement and cable fracture have been simultaneous, whilst many instances will be given where an interruption has occurred at about the same time that an unfelt movement has been recorded on land."

Admiral Wharton's closing remarks offered support for Milne in his quest for *'getting a sufficient number of instruments established in different parts of the world, on which earthquake shocks and tremors can be recorded.'* This is one more major scientific work of Milne's that had tangible benefits for telegraph engineers and ultimately society as a whole. Following the reading of this paper, the Seismological Investigation Committee sent a letter to the Foreign Office for forwarding to other countries. The purpose of the letter was to generate support for the establishment of a global network of seismograph stations.

Seismic Survey of the World

Milne had previously stated publicly that with proper instrumentation it might be possible for large earthquakes to be recorded anywhere on the surface of the earth. In 1889 he was drawn to the work of Ernst von Rebeur-Paschwitz (1861-1895) who had registered distant earthquakes in his Potsdam and Wilhelmshaven observatory. He was also one of the earliest seismologists to have experimented with damping his horizontal pendulum (1892), however, the common application of damping was introduced at a later date. Milne and von Rebeur-Paschwitz frequently corresponded with one another and shortly thereafter Milne was also recording distant earthquakes at his Shide observatory. The work that von Rebeur was doing at the time of his fatal illness prompted Milne to say "*it was during this period of physical incapacity that von Rebeur produced his most remarkable work.*"

In 1894 Ernst von Rebeur-Paschwitz had suggested the foundation of an international organisation of earthquake observatories although nothing came of it because of his premature death in 1895 at the age of 34. However, Milne's paper on *Sub-Oceanic Changes* had focused attention on the kind of work von Rebeur-Paschwitz was doing, especially his notion of a global network of stations. Through the Seismological Investigation Committee, (*Fig. 44*) Milne's strategy for the establishment of a network began in 1896 with the distribution of a circular inviting co-operation from other countries. This was carried out with the kind assistance of the Foreign, Colonial, and India Offices who forwarded the document to many countries and colonies. The result of these communications, together with private correspondence, resulted in instruments being deployed at twenty-two stations. The committee adopted Milne's recommendation that the horizontal pendulum become the adopted standard instrument for the survey so as to prevent unacceptable anomalies that would exist if observatories employed their own seismographs. The instruments at Shide were marked Nos. 1 and 2, but it was only No. 1 that was of the type recommended by the committee. Both had been purchased by Government grants from the Royal Society. Consequently the network of stations grew rapidly attaining a respectable 34 stations, many of which were located in commonwealth countries.

It also occurred to Milne, that accurate time-keeping of global earthquakes was necessary in order to maintain scientific integrity of the data collected. Once again, with the kind assistance of the Foreign Office, the Colonial Office, and the India Office, copies of the following letter on page 79 were circulated throughout the world.

The countries that supported the world-wide network of earthquake recording observatories passed their recorded data on to Milne at Shide where it was analysed, catalogued, and distributed in a bulletin called the Shide Circular (*Fig. 45*) which became a valuable publication in its own right and was issued a total of 27 times. Even with Milne's urging, fewer than a third of all operating seismic stations worldwide cooperated as it was a voluntary effort. The Shide Circulars, despite their shortcomings, remain the only continuous

Seismological Investigation (1897)

— Second Report of the Committee consisting of:

Mr. G. J. SYMONS (Chairman)
Dr. C. DAVISON and **Professor J. MILNE** (Secretaries)
Lord KELVIN, Professor W. G. ADAMS, Mr. J. T. BOTTOMLEY.
Sir F. J. BRAMWELL. Professor G. H. DARWIN, Mr. Horace DARWIN,
Major L. DARWIN, Mr. G. F. DEACON. Professor J. A. EWING.
Professor C. G. KNOTT. Professor G. A. LEBOUR. Professor R. MELDOLA,
Professor J. PERRY. Professor J. H. POYNTING. and Dr. Isaac ROBERTS.

CONTENTS   PAGE

Fig. 44 *Altogether there were eighteen reports of the British Association for the Advancement of Sciences Seismological Investigation Committee between 1896 to 1913. Following Milne's death in 1913, the continuation of work done at Shide and then at Oxford was incorporated into the **International Seismological Summary** in 1918. An annual sum of 10 000 francs was allocated for help with computation and printing. The **International Seismological Association** based in Strassburg was conceived by Dr. G. Gerland & Dr. E. von Rebeur Paschwitz.*

British Association for the Advancement of Science:
Burlington House,
London, W.

Sir, — It is, I think, remarkable that there appears to be no publication which shows the corresponding value in Greenwich mean time of the local time employed throughout the world.

Such a table is indispensable in order to determine accurately the instant of occurrence of earthquakes, sea waves, magnetic phenomena, the despatch of telegrams, and many other events, the sequence of which in absolute time has to be determined.

Although application has been made to the Royal Observatory at Greenwich, to the Royal Geographical Society, to the Central Telegraph Office in London, to the offices of cable companies, and to other possible sources of information, very little has been obtained.

As a Secretary of the British Association Committee whose names are appended, I desire to publish in their forthcoming Report a table showing the differences between Greenwich mean time as used in England and Scotland and that of the civil times used in various parts of the world.

By civil time I mean the time used by railways, telegraphs, and for ordinary public affairs.

If different times are used in various parts of your country, I trust that you will be able to give information relating to the same.

Feeling assured of the value of the table it is intended to compile, I sincerely trust that you will favour me with a full and explicit statement of the time generally employed in your country. If it is mean time, state the meridian ; the observatory, or the place to which this refers; and also, as a check against any misunderstanding, please state distinctly the equivalent of December 1,9 AM. G.M.T. in the local time, or times adopted in your own country.

I have the honour to remain. Sir,
Your obedient servant,
John Milne

British Association for the Advancement of Science

Circular No. 21, *issued by the Seismological Committee,* Professor H. H. TURNER, F.R.S. *(Chairman),* Mr. John MILNE, F.R.S., *Shide, Isle of Wight (Secretary).*

Other worldwide contributions to Shide Circular 21 were from:

San Fernando, Spain	*Ponta Delgada*
St. Miguel. Azores	*Toronto, Ont., Canada*
Victoria, B. C., Canada	*Trinidad, B.W.I.*
Valletta, Malta	*Beirut., Syria*
Cairo, Egypt	*Cape of Good Hope, South Africa*
Bombay, India	*Kodaikanal, Madras, India*
Alipore, Calcutta, India	*Colombo, Ceylon*
Batavia, Java,	*Honolulu, Hawaii*
Sydney, Australia	*Christchurch, New Zealand*

Fig. 45 This Contents page of Shide Circular No. 21 shows all the observatories that were reporting to Milne. The Shide circulars (Nos. 1-27) were produced for the years 1899-1912 and were issued by John Milne from the Shide Observatory. These circulars give simply the records of each observatory without any attempt to collate one with another, except that records which had nothing corresponding at any other observatory were generally struck out. To ascertain this correspondence, or the failure of it, a large ledger was kept by Milne, and ultimately epicentres were determined for those shocks which this ledger showed to be observed at several observatories. These determinations were published in the **BAAS Seismological Investigation Reports.** *Circular 21 records the first entries from Stonyhurst College by the Director, Walter Sidgreaves, SJ.*

compilation of early station bulletins worldwide from 1899 through 1912, totalling over a 1000 pages. These circulars gave the records of each observatory but unfortunately there had been no attempt to collate one with another.

In 1902 the British Government received an invitation to take part in a Conference in Germany. The specific objective was the establishment of an international inquiry on earthquakes. Professor George Howard Darwin (1845-1912), the second son of Charles Darwin and Milne represented Great Britain at the meeting which took place in Strassburg in July 1903. Whilst at Strassburg the British delegates were in no way empowered to pledge His Majesty's Government. On their return to Britain, conference resolutions were considered by the Seismic Committee of the Royal Society. His Majesty's Government was advised to join the German Convention under certain conditions: a) that the United States of America and France are willing to co-operate; and b) that seismology receives State Aid in Britain.

At Shide, Milne continued analysing data received from global observatories which he used to construct world maps (*Fig. 46*) to show where earthquakes occurred. His map descriptions were always factually based as noted by the following: "*In registers from different stations in 1905, as in other years, the number of entries varied within wide limits. In the list for Shide there were 159 entries, but 47 of these refer to extremely minute displacements, the nature of which is uncertain. Disturbances which were undoubtedly of seismic origin came to 112. Out of these 56 were distinctly megaseismic. On the accompanying map (page 82) the origins of 57 widespread movements are indicated. This number represents the annual average for the years 1899 to 1905 inclusive.*"

The thorny subject of financial support for the world-wide network was also tackled by Milne at a Friday evening meeting of the Royal Institution in 1908. At the meeting he stated "*So far as I am aware all foreign stations are subsidised by their respective governments. Great Britain enjoys the cooperation of 45 stations provided with similar instruments which are distributed fairly evenly over the four quarters of the world. The home stations are supported by the British Association, the Royal Society, the Daily Mail, Mr. M. H. Gray and other individuals.*" Professor Milne made no mention of his own substantial financial contribution and the point he was stressing was that his organisation at Shide was not financed by the British government and would benefit from state subsidy.

The weight of administration generated at Shide, curtailed opportunities for Milne to pursue other avenues of advancement in earthquake studies to

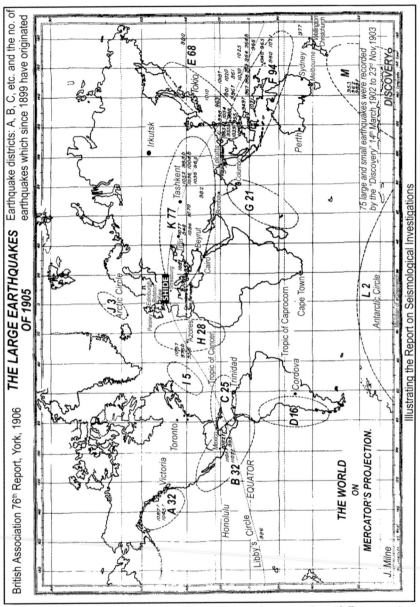

Fig. 46 *The map shows how Milne recorded the information from different stations around the world. From this information Milne concluded that "most earthquakes are confined to a narrow belt running from Central America, to the Azores, the Alpine ranges, Balkan and Himalayan ranges, into the East Indian Archipelago. The quiescence of districts not lying on this band is very marked."*

match the kind of success he had had in Japan. For 25 years since 1875 he had opened many 'seismological windows of opportunity' and now a younger group of seismologists were about to enter the scene and establish fresh fields of investigation.

Life at Shide Hill House

It took a time to adjust to life on the Isle of Wight especially for Toné Milne. Professor Milne had his elderly mother and step-father staying with them so Toné was assured of some companionship whilst the Professor was busy in his observatory. It did not take long for the Milnes to integrate fully into the life of the community. Four local people offered Milne valuable support and friendship: there was William Bullock who helped in construction; Sam Pring assisted Milne in translation of Russian papers; Howard Burgess took care of printing the Shide Circulars; finally there was Johnny Walker, a schoolmaster with a mathematics and geology background. Sam Pring's daughter, Lady Maybury, summed up their friendship when she wrote "*He (Milne) was a very genial, kindly man, immensely popular because of his humour and joie de vivre which he had the gift of communicating to other people. Anyone who worked with him became his devoted slave and was rewarded by a real friendship.*"

Professional colleagues, in particular Professor John Perry and Professor Herbert Hall Turner (1861-1930) would come to Shide Hill House as often as work permitted. There were also many casual visitors (newspaper reporters) and experts in the field of seismology from all parts of the world who called in on Milne for a variety of reasons. The status of certain distinguished visitors is clearly noted in the guestbook that Milne kept. One such notable entry is that of Prince Boris Galitzin (1862-1916), the founding father of Russian seismology who developed the first electro-magnetic instrument and developed the first seismic recording network in Russia.

In 1896 John Johnson Shaw (1873-1948) came into contact with Professor Milne whilst on holiday on the Isle of Wight and they became lifelong friends. Shaw, inspired by the work of Milne, returned to his West Bromwich home (near Birmingham) and converted his cellar into a science laboratory. Within a few weeks Shaw had built his first seismograph from everyday objects found around the house. His seismograph was powered by an old clock and the recording drum was made from an empty Tate and Lyle's treacle tin. The other parts of the seismograph came from parts of an old bicycle frame. J.J.Shaw was a pawnbroker by profession (and an amateur seismologist now).

Fig. 47 *Japanese visitors to Shide. Toné Milne is seated with John standing to the right and his dog Billy to the left. Credit: Patrick Nott*

He continued throughout the years to work in close partnership with Milne and together they developed the Milne-Shaw Seismograph (*Figs. 55 to 60*) in 1913 which went on to become the world's standard earthquake recording instrument for a considerable length of time. Unfortunately, the launch of the Milne-Shaw seismograph at Shide coincided with the sad death of Professor John Milne.

For Toné Milne, visitors from Japan were always especially welcome as she was always glad to receive word from her home country. Both Baron Dairoku Kikuchi (1855-1917), a former graduate of Cambridge University in 1877, and Fusakichi Ōmori (Milne's protégé) made the pilgrimage to Shide. Another distinguished visitor to Milne's observatory was Mrs. Lou Henry Hoover (1874-1944) who became the First Lady of the United States following her marriage to Herbert Hoover (also a mining engineer and President of the United States from 1929 to 1933). She was the first woman to publish a paper in the Bulletin of the Seismological Society of America (on John Milne). Lou Henry interviewed Milne and went on to write an article describing Milne's travels in Japan and his work with the Seismological Society of Japan. This interview was published as *John Milne, Seismologist* and appeared in BSSA, Volume 2, No. 1, pages 2–7 and from that paper she states *"It is quaint conceit that to the utter quiet of this pretty, tree-encircled old house, with its grassy stone-stepped terraces leading down towards the little valley, with the great peaceful downs rising at its back, should come the earthquakes of the world to be classified and studied. But come they do, and a vast amount of work they make for Professor Milne and his clever Japanese assistant, Mr. Hirota. There are about 60 stations whose reports come, some monthly, some twice yearly and some when a chance boat might bring them. These must all be carefully correlated and filed away, and every six months a circular containing all the recent registers is sent out to all the stations. This is practically a labour of love on Professor Milne's part. He holds no official position."* The final statement by Mrs. Hoover is a reminder that the observatory was not a government establishment.

Fig. 48 *John and Toné Milne at Shide Hill House.*
Credit: Seismological Society of America
Taken from John Milne, Seismologist by Mrs. Lou Henry Hoover (1912)

Lou Henry Hoover intrigued by the number of visitors who travelled long distances to meet Professor Milne commented: "*From the leaves of his visitors book, turned over during his few minutes of absence, one cannot but be interested in the dozens of names in the past few weeks, which appear but an average sample. From all parts of England these pilgrim questioners come; from Scotland and Ireland; all the great universities are represented - Edinburgh, Glasgow, Cambridge, Oxford, Sheffield, University College of London, and Bristol University, Corfu in Greece, Bermuda, Milan, Paris, Pennsylvania, and Greenwich Observatory; jostling one another are the names from all the pages of one's geography, come to do homage to a man who is interested in all of them.*" Had Mrs. Hoover had more time to peruse the visitors' guest book she would have noticed the names of Edward, Prince of Wales, a naval cadet at the time of his visit; Baron Ryochi Kujo, a brother-in-Law of the Emperor of Japan, and Professor Harry Fielding Reid of Stanford University who had a key role to play following the San Francisco earthquake of 1906.

The Antarctic explorer, Captain Robert Scott (1868–1912) also visited Shide Hill House (*Fig. 49*). Scott's contact with Milne was desired on the basis that he would take a Milne seismograph (No. 37) with him on his 'Discovery expedition of the Antarctic' (1901-1904). The seismograph was installed in one of the magnetic huts in Victoria Land, about 15 miles from Mount Erebus. The instrument was in the charge of Mr. Louis Bernacchi who was attached to the SS Discovery. Although observations were made under exceptional difficulties, Mr. Bernacchi nevertheless managed to return with about 3 000 feet of photographic film. Of the 136 Antarctic earthquakes recorded, none had been felt by the Discovery personnel. The Antarctic data was taken to Shide for further analysis by Milne and his assistants Hirota and Howard Burgess of Newport.

In 1908, Milne seismograph No. 37 was transported from the Antarctic to Stonyhurst College, Hurst Green, which is 5 km south-west of Clitheroe in the picturesque Ribble valley. The college spent £36 on improvements before it was finally installed in the transept of their observatory (*Fig. 50*). It was set up in a dry underground magnetic chamber which was not as susceptible to variations of temperature. The seismograph was placed on a pillar composed of two cut stones firmly cemented together. On the top of these there was a slate slab cemented to the uppermost stone. The pillar was embedded in and rested upon 12 inches (30 cm) of concrete below the stone floor of the chamber and the concrete was set onto hard clayey soil. The height of the top of the slab from the floor was 3½ feet (107 cm) and its height above

Fig. 49 *Left to right: Captain Robert Scott, John Milne, James Arnott (Milne's stepfather), John Perry. Toné Milne is seated. Credit: Patrick Nott*

sea-level was 364 feet (111 metres). The operation of the Milne seismograph ceased in 1924 only to be replaced by a Milne-Shaw instrument in 1928. Recording of earthquakes at Stonyhurst College was suspended in 1947 due to the retirement and death of Father Rowland.

Life at Shide was not all work and no play. Professor Milne enjoyed croquet with his wife and guests on the lawns of his house, however, golf was probably his main recreational activity. He usually took along his dog, a white fox-terrier called 'Billy' who proved an excellent retriever of lost golf balls. Prior to setting off for a round of golf, the canny Professor would coat his golf balls in aniseed or some other substance that was easily detected by Billie's nose! Unfortunately his dog died in 1904 and the sadness Milne felt in his loss inspired him to write an obituary which appeared in Golf Illustrated.

Howard Burgess who printed the Shide Circular was also the Editor of 'Fore', the local golfing magazine. He published an article written by Johnny Walker about Professor Milne in Fore. The article described a British Association

Fig. 50 *Stonyhurst College Observatory, Hurst Green, Ribble Valley, Lancashire, where the Milne and Milne–Shaw seismographs were housed. Credit: Yvonne James*

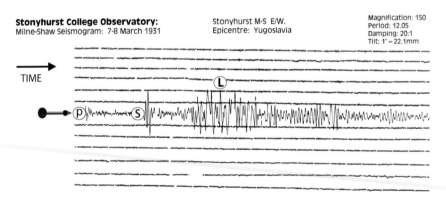

Stonyhurst College Observatory:
Milne-Shaw Seismogram: 7-8 March 1931

Stonyhurst M-S E/W.
Epicentre: Yugoslavia

Magnification: 150
Period: 12.05
Damping: 20:1
Tilt: 1" = 22.1mm

TIME

Fig. 51 *Stonyhurst seismogram of the 8th March 1931 Yugoslavia Earthquake. Obtained from the Milne–Shaw seismograph.*

Adapted from Earthquakes and other Earth Movement (Milne, J / Lee, A.W., 1939). Kegan Paul, Trench, Trübner & Co. Ltd.

meeting in South Africa in 1905 in which a party of distinguished scientists' (Milne was one of them) took part in a sight-seeing trip to Victoria Falls. It was here that Milne apparently came up with the idea of driving a golf ball from one side of the falls to the other. As you are aware, Milne was well known for his sense of humour, so if this did actually take place it would no doubt prove a fitting entry into the Guinness Book of Records!

With kind regards, Mr. & Mrs. Milne.

SHIDE, ISLE OF WIGHT, ENGLAND.

Fig. 52 *John and Toné Milne enjoying a quiet stroll. Credit: Patrick Nott*

Socialising was always top of the agenda for Milne, especially when it involved a drop of whiskey at the Royal Victoria Yacht Club at Ryde of which he was a member. The Yacht Club was used for one of his experiments which involved the installation of a seismograph in the cellar in order to investigate tidal loading. The seismograph on one occasion registered violent tremors. Milne was puzzled because none of his other seismographs had registered a tremor of similar magnitude. The yacht club seismograph showed no further movement until the same day the following week and at the same time. Milne deduced that whatever was causing this must be a local phenomenon. He explored a number of possible scenarios such as quarry blasting, traffic in town, and even Royal Navy exercises in the waters of the Solent before eventually arriving at the answer from a quite unexpected source — the butler and the housekeeper were both off duty at the same time!

Both Milne and 'Snowy' Hirota were keen photographers and had learned a great deal from their friend William Bullock. The Professor's enthusiasm for photography was rewarded when he was made President of the Isle of Wight Photographic Society. As an experienced photographer, he even recognised that some areas of processing photographs offered tangible improvements in the processing of seismograms. This was typical of Milne to see beyond his hobby to the benefit of the British Association and seismology in general.

It was fitting that Milne was now considered by many to be the 'Master of Seismology' and such distinguished service surely was worthy of recognition of some form or another. Further honours did in fact come Milne's way; firstly from The Royal Society who presented the Professor with the coveted Royal Medal, secondly, Oxford University awarded him an honorary D.Sc., and finally, the University of Tokyo made Milne an Emeritus Professor.

John Milne visited Rochdale about once a year. Following one such visit in 1910, an article in the Rochdale Times quoted Milne " . . . *it is only the old men like your late mayor, Colonel Fishwick who knows me. I wander through the market, look at Syke's shop. Think of Rushbearing and Old Ben, who used to drive me from the Red Lion to the Tim Bobbin when on my way to Tunshill, but I feel I am absolutely alone. Old Vicar Molesworth has gone, and even Rowan, of St. James. Zac Mellor was my last friend. Zac Mellor has gone also, and I go into the Wellington, take a drink, come out, and no one knows me. Still, I wish Rochdale all prosperity.*"

Shinobu 'Snowy' Hirota was perhaps Milne's closest friend and his constant companionship skill and dedication in maintaining earthquake instruments and interpreting seismograms was a major factor in the seismological successes that Milne enjoyed. They were together for 17 years until, due to ill health, Snowy returned to Japan on the 16th December 1912. Sadly Shinobu Hirota passed away shortly after arriving home. The health of Professor Milne was not too good either. Blinding headaches had begun to plague him to the point where they never really went away. He kept Toné in the dark about how ill he really was and blamed his condition on 'just an attack of the feebles.' In fact Milne was suffering from Bright's disease which is a kidney disease first described in 1827 by the English Physician, Richard Bright.

By mid July 1913 the disease confined Milne to bed. Burgess kept Shaw informed on Milne's deteriorating health and on the 31st July 1913 Professor John Milne lapsed into a coma and died aged 62. The funeral took place in the parish church of St. Thomas à Becket in Newport and he was later interred in the church yard of St. Paul's, Barton, in an adjacent plot to his mother and step-father. The mourners came from all walks of life. The Emperor of Japan sent Baron Kujo as his representative and a little girl from London sent a small bouquet simply inscribed 'For Dear Uncle John Earthquakes'. Toné received many letters and telegrams of condolence including one from the Japanese Ambassador, Mr. K. Inouye stating: *"Please accept my deepest sympathy on the great calamity which has befallen you. It is not only an irreparable loss to this country and to the scientific world but also to Japan where his name will never be forgotten."* Moreover the whole front page of the Daily Mirror, 1st August 1913, was devoted to the death of Professor John Milne!

In 1914 BAAS Seismological Investigation Committee published the following: *"The death of John Milne in July 1913 creates a situation of some difficulty and anxiety. He organised a world-wide seismological service with very little financial help from others. In many of the outlying stations the instrumental equipment was provided either by himself or by one of his friends, and the care of it has been generously undertaken by a volunteer who is often busily engaged in other work. The collation of results was in the early years undertaken by Milne himself, with the able help of Shinobu Hirota. Of late years a subsidy of 200 l a year from Government Grant Fund allowed paid assistants; and Shinobu Hirota thus obtained a well-deserved official position; but for many years the only salary that he received was paid from Milne's own pocket."*

Professor John Milne's sudden death sent 'shock waves' through the academic community. The President of the International Seismological Association at the time of Milne's death was Prince Boris Galitzin. He reflected on Milne's academic achievements by emphasising the exceptional work that he had done in establishing seismology as a new and important branch of geophysics. On the other hand, Professor John Perry commented on the kind of man Milne was: *"Milne's success was greatly due to his power to interest all sorts of people in his work .... He took an interest in all scientific work and perhaps he thought too highly of the work of other men .... He was very modest and had always had time for other people .... In Japan and at Shide he was always very hospitable."*

It was essential that Milne's work should be continued. Leading geophysicists such as Professor Judd and Professor Geikie encouraged Professor Turner, the Chairman of the British Association Seismological Committee, to take care of Shide Observatory. For reasons of economy and convenience the observatory was eventually moved from the Isle of Wight to Oxford in 1919.

Toné Milne had to face new challenges in adapting to life without her husband. She was glad of the extra support she received following the arrival of her nephew, Jodo Horikawa. For Toné, the transfer of the observatory to Oxford was sufficient enough reason for her to return to Japan. John Milne's *will* made Toné financially secure with a guaranteed income for life arranged by the Trustees through the Daiichi Bank in Japan. Most of Professor Milne's scientific books and instruments were left to the British Association.

The influence of Professor John Milne extends far beyond his own contribution to science and seismology. The founding of the Seismological Society of Japan, which in turn led to the formation of the Imperial Earthquake Investigation Committee and the organising of the first International Network of Seismological Observatories throughout the world no doubt gave Milne great satisfaction. Above all, his personal influence on those with whom he came in contact with, his guidance, inspiration and devotion has without doubt earned him the right to be called the '*Father of Modern Seismology*.'

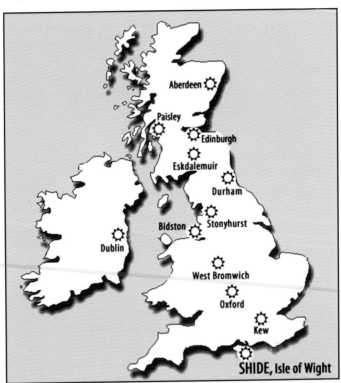

Fig. 53 *Early 20ᵗʰ century British seismological observatories.*

Chapter 5

After Milne

Milne's major work was accomplished in seismically active Japan. Britain on the other hand, being comparatively free from seismic activity, was perhaps one reason why his scientific contributions were undervalued. In Japan Milne had a penchant for seeking out opinions and observations of fellow scientists; in fact he preferred working with others whereas in England he often felt isolated. There was also a lack of seismologists of his calibre with whom he could engage in constructive scientific debate. Inevitably, he became a lone worker in what was to the British an obscure field of research. Life on the Isle of Wight may have been good for the family and scientific research, but it distanced him from other active scientific communities.

After the First World War the Shide Observatory was transferred to Oxford and Toné Milne returned to Japan thus all ties to the Isle of Wight were effectively severed. Toné and John had no children and John Milne himself was an only child. His birthplace in Liverpool has been re-developed; Tunshill House was demolished presumably to make way for the M62 motorway and the original part of Shide Hill House has been pulled down. Only 147 Drake Street in Rochdale still stands but bears no indication of a connection with its distinguished former occupant.

In 1927, Charles Davison was encouraged by Sir Archibald Geikie to write the book *The Founders of Seismology*. Chapter 10 of Davison's book is devoted to the work of Milne. Davison writes "*In the new epoch, then opening, when seismology demanded the whole energy of its supporters as well as their active cooperation, it is not, I think, too much to claim that Milne lifted the science to an altogether different and higher plane*" and he concludes with "*The influence of a leader in science extends far beyond his own contributions. In founding the Seismological Society of Japan, which led to the formation of the Imperial Earthquake Investigation Committee, and in organising the network of stations throughout the world, and above all, in his personal influences on those with whom he came in touch, it seems to me possible that seismology may owe almost as much to his guidance and inspiration as it does to the incessant labour of his well-spent life.*"

Professor John Milne is still remembered in Japan. In 1926 a service was held and a memorial to the memory of John and Toné Milne was erected in Hakodate cemetery, Hokkaido. In the cemetery there is an information board erected in honour of John and Toné Milne which reads as follows:

John and Toné Milne

In 1876 an English man named John Milne was invited by the Engineering Ministry to teach mining engineering and geology at Kobu University and Tokyo Teikoku University. Becoming interested in the study of earthquakes in Japan, he invented a seismometer and made seismological observations all over Japan. He is also known as one of the founders of seismology in Japan, and helped establish the Seismological Society of Japan in 1880.

In 1877 he came to Hakodate to conduct geological research. The following year he returned to Hakodate to survey the shell mounds of an ancient indigenous settlement. In 1881 he married Toné, the eldest daughter of Jokyo Horikawa, in Tokyo and in 1895 he returned to England with her.

After his death in 1913, Toné's health deteriorated and she returned to Hakodate, where she lived until she passed away in 1919.

The tombstones for Mr. & Mrs. Milne and Jokyo Horikawa are in this graveyard.

CITY OF HAKODATE

More recently in 1974 the University of Tokyo donated a number of 'Prunus Kanzan' cherry tree saplings to be planted at Shide and the Isle of Wight College of Arts and Technology as a 'living memorial' to the great seismologist. This was carried out by Mr. Haruki Mori, the Japanese Ambassador to Great Britain who also laid a wreath on Milne's grave at St. Paul's Barton church where he is buried. The plaque at Shide reads:

PRUNUS KANZAN
Presented by the University of Tokyo in memory of
Professor John Milne (1850-1913). The Father of Seismology, of the Imperial College Tokyo and of Shide Isle of Wight and was planted by his Excellency the Japanese Ambassador 14 March 1974.

Fig. 54 *The Japanese Ambassador to Great Britain pay their respects to John Milne at St. Paul's church. Credit: Patrick Nott*

Milne the person was poetically summed up in *Eminent Living Geologists, Professor John Milne, D.Sc. F.R.S., F.G.S., Hon. Fellow of King's College, London* as published in the Geological Magazine, Decade V, Vol. **IX**, No. 578. pp. 337-46, August 1912 by the following: *"What is the secret of his attractiveness and his perennial youth? It is the cheerful light-heartedness of his disposition, which has never deserted him in all these years, but has sustained his spirit and given him the power to infect others with the same interest and enthusiasm in his work and carry them along with him.*

The phenomena of earthquakes are at once his serious study and his delightful occupation. For him the earth is like an Aeolian harp, it vibrates to the influence of every heavenly body, it is played upon by the sun's tropic rays, buffeted by the unruly ocean in its lap, resounds to the stress of the storm-winds, is shaken by earthquakes and volcanoes from pole to pole, yet repeats, by a tender throb to his seismometer at Shide, the faintest vibration even from a distance of twelve thousand miles away."

The Oxford headquarters of the new organisation under the direction of Professor Herbert Turner became known as the International Seismological Summary. British observatories continued to play a vital part in the new worldwide network and important research was performed on site noise, microseisms, etc. by comparing seismograms written at the various stations in Britain and applying the results to all British Association stations.

From 1895 when Milne set up his first observatory at Shide, within two or three years, other stations such as Edinburgh, Kew, Paisley and Bidston were established. All these places had astronomical and / or meteorological observatories to provide an accurate source of timing for seismograph recordings. Meanwhile J.J. Shaw was conducting important work in his cellar in West Bromwich where he was mainly testing seismographs that he had built or modified. As you may recall the original seismograph used to equip the British Association observatories was the Milne horizontal pendulum. The performance of this instrument was limited owing to its lack of damping. Shaw incorporated electromagnetic damping to the Milne design and

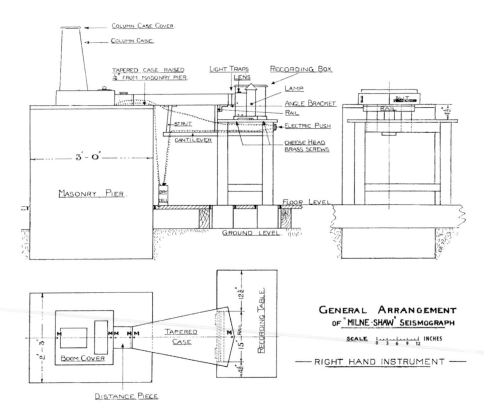

Fig. 55 *Milne-Shaw Seismograph: general arrangement diagram.*
Credit: Lapworth Museum of Geology

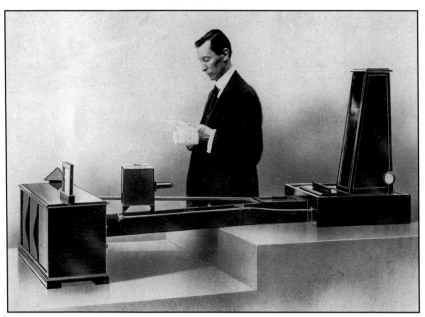

Fig. 56 Milne–Shaw Seismograph: general arrangement.
Credit: Lapworth Museum of Geology

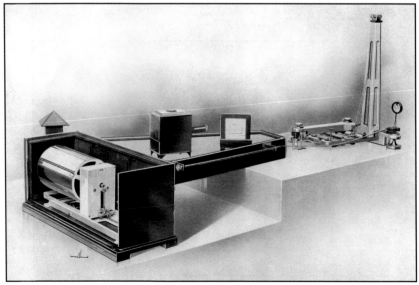

Fig. 57 Milne–Shaw Seismograph: general arrangement with case removed.
Credit: Lapworth Museum of Geology

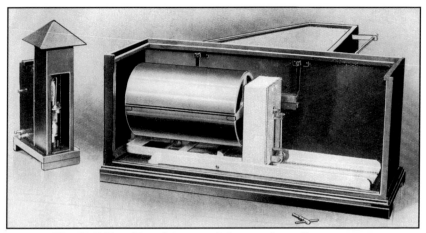

Fig. 58 Milne-Shaw Seismograph: lamp and recording apparatus.
Credit: Lapworth Museum of Geology

Fig. 59 Milne-Shaw Seismograph: horizontal pendulum and damping device.
Credit: Lapworth Museum of Geology

increased its gain, thereby greatly enhancing the usefulness of the device. The newly developed instrument was installed in Milne's Shide observatory and became known as the Milne-Shaw Horizontal Pendulum Seismograph.

Today, old bulletins containing seismogram data can be used for event relocation as our technique for earthquake location improves. They are also useful for magnitude analysis in order to establish a consistent magnitude scale. Even the very early bulletin data from mostly undamped seismographs before 1900 can be used to determine event magnitudes. The value of old bulletins to modern seismology can therefore still play a part in seismic risk studies, especially if the catalogues of earthquake data are as complete as possible.

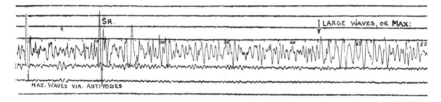

Fig. 60 *Milne-Shaw record: 24ᵗʰ November, 1914, Bidston, UK. Credit: Lapworth Museum of Geology*

The pioneering work of Professor John Milne was also the cornerstone of a revolution in our understanding of the dynamic earth. Milne's network of seismographs ushered in the ability to detect and locate earthquakes by remote sensing which today has become an extremely valuable means of collecting information (remote sensing is the utilization at a distance of any device for gathering information about the environment from instruments such as those found on board aircraft and spacecraft). There were now opportunities for future scientists to probe into the Earth's inner structure and the accumulation of decades of information on all aspects of earthquake science eventually came together into a unified theory which is known today as Plate Tectonics.

The move towards the 'grand synthesis of plate tectonics' began to gather pace at the start of World War I when scientists developed a model of concentric layers of core, mantle and surface crust. The earth's surface came under scrutiny in 1915 when the German meteorologist Alfred Wegener published *The Origins of Continents and Oceans* in which he postulated the radical idea of continental drift. By 1929 his ideas had the support of Arthur Holmes who suggested that convective flow of heated rock within the mantle was the driving force for the "drift". Rapid strides were made in the early 1950's when research work into magnetism in rocks revealed that polar wander was consistent with Wegener's drift theory and in the late 1950's the first detailed maps of the mid-ocean ridge system were produced.

The 1960's saw the establishment of the concept of sea-floor spreading by Harry Hess (1906-1969), a professor of geology at Princeton University and the British geologists Frederick Vine (b. 1939) and Drummond Matthews (1931-1997). Based on this work, Canadian geophysicist J. Tuzo Wilson (1908-1993) introduced the idea of 'plates' which ultimately led to the revolutionary concept of Plate Tectonics. The contribution made by French geophysicist Xavier Le Pichon (b. 1937), Dan McKenzie (b. 1942) of Cambridge University and W. Jason Morgan (b. 1935) at Princeton University in the USA was to define the individual shape of the plates. Plate tectonics explains virtually all of Earth's major geological features and makes sense of otherwise inexplicable phenomena such as earthquakes, volcanic eruptions and the formation of mountain ranges. Plate tectonics has also led to new discoveries such as that of the hydrothermal vent organisms and their implications for our understanding of life on the planet — outcomes that investigators such as John Milne, Alfred Wegener, or Harry Hess could not have predicted as they followed their scientific curiosity.

The ever-present threat of more earthquakes in Japan is directly influenced by the position of four tectonic plates *(Fig. 61)* - the North American (Okhotsk), the Eurasian (Amurian), the Pacific, and the Philippine Sea plates. The former two continental plates are colliding on Honshū (the geographical position of the Mino-Owari earthquake coincides fairly well with the boundary of both these plates). Professor Milne had previously shown that most earthquakes were generated along the eastern sea-board of Japan. This is easily explained today by the subduction of the Pacific and Philippine Plates beneath the continental plates. This complex tectonic activity accounts for the majority of earthquakes as well as for the extensive volcanism that helped create the Japanese islands.

Experts in the field of geophysics and hazard research are actively engaged in planning and implementing strategies for dealing with future destructive global geophysical events which pose a potentially bigger threat today than when John Milne was alive. After the Mino-Owari earthquake of 1891, the next devastating earthquake to hit Japan was in 1923 when Tokyo and the neighbouring city of Yokohama were virtually obliterated by the Great Kanto Earthquake in the worst natural disaster in the country's history. The quake destroyed 300 000 buildings including 20 000 factories and 1 500 schools. Out of a population of 11.7 million, 101 000 were killed and a further 52 000 injured, with 3.2 million people left homeless. The cities of Yokohama and Tokyo have now largely merged to form the Greater Tokyo metropolitan region; a gigantic agglomeration of 33 million people. If and when another catastrophic earthquake strikes it will probably make the Kanto earthquake of 1923 look small by comparison.

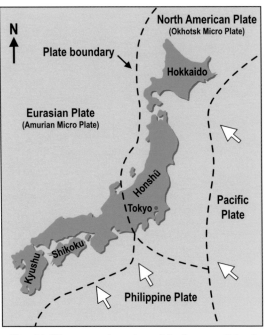

Fig. 61 *Plate tectonic setting of the Japanese Islands: based on Fig. 2 from "Can the Okhotsk plate be discriminated from the North American plate?" Seno, T., Sakurai, T. and Stein, S. (1996)*

At the time of writing this book it is 100 years since Milne's Bakerian lecture *"Recent Advances in Seismology"* given to the Royal Society on the 22nd March 1906. In the early part of his lecture Professor Milne described Mallet's work on the Neapolitan Earthquake of 1859 before going on to state: *"But little further progress was made until 1880, when as a side issue of Japan's material development along western lines, Seismology began to grow with great rapidity into its present form and became a distinct branch of observational science. In that year the Seismological Society of Japan was founded."* It's quite remarkable that the foundations of seismology were established as a 'side issue' in Japan's economic development.

Professor John Milne deserves our gratitude for his tireless effort in pioneering effective means of studying and monitoring of earthquake threats and having the awareness of basic contingency planning in his consideration of buildings and building material.

Fig 62 *John Milne: (Credit: E. A. Kime, Isle of Wight).*

Born: 30th December 1850
Professor John Milne, D.Sc. F.R.S., F.G.S.
Hon. Fellow of King's College, London.
Died: 31st July 1913

Appendix 1

Milne–MacDonald Vibration Recorder

By 1889 Professor Milne had carried out numerous investigations with instruments for monitoring vibratory motions with particular reference to their effects on buildings and bridges. Through his research work in this area Milne designed the Milne Seismometer in 1889 to investigate the vibrations of buildings and bridges resulting from earthquake tremors or artificial disturbances.

Whilst pursuing his study of vibrations of buildings, Milne became interested in the vibrations of railway carriages and locomotives. At the same time Mr. John MacDonald of the Locomotive Department of Tokyo Railways was also conducting experiments to reduce the vibration of steam engines. This project proved irresistible to Milne and without hesitation he offered his services to MacDonald. They worked together to perfect an instrument on the same principle as the seismograph for recording locomotive vibrations.

Their collaborative efforts produced the Milne-MacDonald Vibration Recorder. It was a small compact instrument of considerable stability that was designed not to be as sensitive as a seismograph. Its operation was based upon a clockwork motor slowly driving round a recording drum. A sheet of paper wrapped around the drum was marked by three pencils attached to the tips of pointers. The traces produced by the pointers represent the vertical and horizontal vibrations made by the locomotive.

Milne and MacDonald conducted numerous trials on different tracks in Japan. Their results confirmed not only imbalances but variations in the speed of trains. The recognition of imbalance was a major step forward as safe working speeds could now be established. Another benefit of using such a device was in pinpointing faults on the track. After a few minor modifications, Milne offered the instrument to the Japanese railway authorities.

During a visit to Britain in 1889 Milne demonstrated his new device for registering the three components of oscillation on a railway train to his friend Sir William Thompson on a railway journey from Largs to Glasgow. As a result of this demonstration it was suggested to Milne that he present his findings to the Institute of Civil Engineers in London. Milne's paper '*On the vibratory Movement of Locomotives and on Timing of Trains and Testing Railway Tracks*' was presented to the Institute in November 1890. The ensuing discussion was of great interest to the audience of eminent engineers of the Institution that its committee honoured both authors with a coveted prize, The Telford Premium, which was a monetary award that took its name from the Institute's first president.

Although this wasn't the first attempt to produce such an instrument to measure the vibrations of trains, the Milne-MacDonald Vibration Recorder was by far the most successful and sophisticated. The instrument was manufactured by R.C. Munro and Co., London and subsequently universally deployed on British lines and abroad. Milne and MacDonald found that they had under-estimated the amplitude of the vibrations of rolling stock on Japanese railways. The device was modified by incorporating a stronger spring and an increase in mass.

His work with MacDonald in producing the vibration recorder, is a good example of Milne being able to adapt his skills and knowledge gained in one specialist field for good purpose in another.

Appendix 2

A book on John Milne's life and work would be incomplete without reference to his delight in writing science-based fiction. An early example of this was discovered amongst remnants recovered from the fire that destroyed his home in Tokyo. A fire-damaged notebook revealed that from his earlier Iceland visit, Milne had drafted a manuscript describing his 'youthful wanderings'. Under consideration for a title for the manuscript were '*Wanderings in known and unknown Iceland*' and '*Iceland, or the scramblings of a lunatic.*'

His writing style matured considerably during his tenure as Professor at the Imperial College. The Editor of the Japan Mail, an English language newspaper, was a close friend of Milne's and it was he that encouraged Milne to write a series of short stories about a mad scientist called John Henry Fizzles. A common thread running through all the 'yarns' that Milne wrote was that telling the story took precedent over the adequacy of his writing.

Mark Kershaw: Colonial Facts & Fictions: Humorous Sketches

Ann Kershaw was John Milne's grandmother. This probably explains why Milne chose Mark Kershaw as his pseudonym when he wrote the book *Colonial Facts and Fictions: Humorous Sketches* published by Chatto and Windus, Piccadilly, London, 1886. My first insight into this book came from a reviewers comment found on the web – "*He (Milne) emphasizes the fact that our two feet are rarely identical in size, and that therefore a shoemaker who measures only one foot is a bungler.*"

The book is a record of Milne's observations of life during an extensive visit to Australia, Tasmania and New

Fig. 63 *Front cover of the book: 1886.*

Zealand. Professor John Perry described the book as being light-hearted and full of amusing anecdotes; an ideal book which could be put to one side without serious loss of continuity.

One of the stories in the book is called *Adventures with a Boomerang*. It describes the occasion in which Milne had a boomerang given to him in Brisbane.

"I had a boomerang given to me when in Brisbane. I have got it yet. If the troubles it has caused me, and the troubles it has in store for me, do not bring me to an early grave, I have the intention of passing this specimen of aboriginal workmanship on to some fellow I don't like. By the same messenger I intend to send him the address of a respectable undertaker. If you have a deadly hatred for a man — if there is a man who has insulted you, called you a liar and a thief, converted you and your family into paupers, blasted your hopes for this world and the future — just ask him, when he goes to Australia, to bring you a boomerang. Tell him you would like a good big one — a fighting boomerang. He will either be dead or imprisoned before he gets back. My boomerang is a fighting boomerang. It is made out of very hard wood. At both ends it is pointed. The edge of it is like that of a sword, and it is shaped like a young moon. My troubles with this thing began in the streets of Brisbane. It would not go in any of my portmanteaus, so I tied it on the outside of my bag. The bag then became like a double-ended ram pointed at both ends. The first notice I received about my double-ended ram was from an old gentleman against whom my bag happened to bump. 'D—n it, sir, what's that? You've torn my trousers,' said he. I apologized, and felt very mean. I shall never forget the way in which that old man glared through his spectacles, first at me, then at his trousers, and then at the double-ender. The last look decided the course I should take. I might charge him. After this I tried to be more careful, and got on pretty well until I reached the station.

At the ticket-office I found myself in a crowd, and, the persons behind pushing me, drove the double-ender into the legs and hinder parts of those in front. The way in which they jumped and squirmed was quite ridiculous. 'Please excuse me; it's only a boomerang,' I said. 'Boomerang be hanged!' said one man. 'What do you mean by bringing a thing like that for in here?' By and by it got generally known that there was a man with a boomerang in a bag coming through the crowd, and they made a passage for us. The amount of apologies that I made for my boomerang during the next six or seven days nearly killed me. Every time I made a move into a railway-carriage, out of a railway-carriage, near to a group of people where there was not much room, I had always to herald myself by, 'Ah! please excuse me — ahem! I've got a boomerang.' Once the bag got a side-blow, and swung round to catch me across the calf of the leg; the result of which was that for decency's sake I had to borrow some pins to fasten up the rent. It is useless to say that the trousers and my leg were both spoiled. My leg got better, but the trousers didn't. It cost me twenty-six shillings for a new pair. Once or twice I thought of throwing the thing away; but as I heard that boomerangs come circling back towards the thrower, my courage failed me. To have a thing weighing forty pounds, with the shape and edge of a scimitar, cavorting about your head, was not to be risked. If I had paid a man to throw it away for me, I might have been indicted for manslaughter. I would sooner be mated to a tinted Venus or a Frankenstein than to a good-sized boomerang.

Since the above experience I have tried the thing, and thus far it has not exhibited a trace of the movement attributed to Noah's dove. At first I only threw it two or three feet; but as I gained courage I threw it farther — first edgeways, then sideways, flatways, point-ways, straight-ways, upwards, downwards, obliquely forwards, backwards, upwards, outwards, and in some fifty or sixty other manners and directions, but invariably with the result that I had to walk after the confounded thing and bring it back. I was afraid to leave the weapon behind—it might kill somebody. I believe I have walked one thousand seven hundred miles after that boomerang. The only way in which I have been successful in inducing a boomerang to return to me has been either by paying a man to fetch it, or else by tying a long string to it. After this it is needless to say that the return of the boomerang is a myth, and as a myth let us relegate it to the land of the unicorn and the deadly upas."

NOTE.—Since writing the above I met with a gentleman who declares that boomerangs are capable of returning, not simply once, but repeatedly. The difficulty, in his mind, was how to prevent them from returning. 'There were tame boomerangs and frisky boomerangs,' he remarked. My boomerang was probably a tame one. If his boomerang had not knocked over two policemen and dispersed a crowd, he would at this moment have been the inmate of a gaol. It came about in this way. 'Do you see,' said he, 'Christmas was drawing nigh, and I thought I would buy something to amuse the kids. Well, I went into a big toy-shop at the corner of Market Street, and, after looking at a lot of mechanical dolls, rocking-horses, and what not, I decided on taking a boomerang. The young lady, who wrapped it up in a sheet of stiff brown paper, remarked that I had selected one that was rather lively. It was just getting dark when I got in the bus, and I put the parcel containing the boomerang on my knee. Once or twice I observed that the thing began to edge along sideways towards the lap of an old lady, who was my neighbour. "That parcel of yours seems to be fidgetty," said she. At that moment it gave a jump. "0 lor'!" said the old lady; "why, it's alive!" "Don't be alarmed, mum," said I; "it's quite harmless;" and I put both hands over my purchase to keep it quiet. "It's only a boomerang that I bought to amuse the children." At the word boomerang everybody looked as if they had received an electric shock. One young man put up his eyeglass, an old gentleman looked over his spectacles, the old lady shot open her umbrella, and everybody edged away. If I had said it was an infernal machine the consternation could not have been greater. "Oh, you wicked young man!" said the old lady, still keeping up her umbrella as a shield; but just then the bus stopped at the corner of my street, so, wishing my companions good-night, I got out, feeling, as you may suppose, much relieved. My wife opened the door for me. "Maria," says I, "I've brought a boomerang just to amuse you and the children." "Oh, you darling" and she threw her arms round my neck. What she thought a boomerang was I don't know; but while she was dangling on my neck, the parcel slipped from beneath my arm and dropped on the floor.

As to the exact sequence of events which followed this unfortunate accident, I have but a hazy recollection. For a moment or two the parcel bobbed up and down on the floor, until the top of the boomerang stuck through the paper, when off it went with a whizz, gyrating, waltzing, twisting, and turning in all directions, round and round the room. Maria was stretched flat; I got two bangs on the head, but managed to crawl beneath the sofa; the cat was killed, the chandelier was smashed, every ornament was cleared from the shelves. Then it paused, balancing itself on one of its tops on the corner of the sideboard. All of a sudden an idea seemed to strike it, and off it set upstairs. For the next ten minutes I had the pleasure of listening to my Christmas present smashing and banging round every room from the first floor up to the attics. The servant-maids and the children had luckily escaped to the cellar. Suddenly the noise stopped, and Maria, who had found me beneath the sofa, suggested that the Christmas present was taking breath. "This ain't particular paradise, Maria," said I. "Oh, Tom, let us run into the street and call assistance." Just as we had got from beneath the sofa, we heard a hop-hop-hop on the top story. The boomerang was evidently coming down-stairs "Shut the door!" said Maria; and I did, but only just in time. When I looked through the keyhole I could see Boomey with a bit of string and a streamer or two of brown paper round its neck, sitting on the bottom stair. At that moment there was a fearful knocking at the front door, and the boomerang raised itself on end and hopped off along the passage, as if it expected more sport. Maria ran to the window, and said, "Good gracious, Tom, there's two policemen!" Throw them my latch-key," said I, "and tell them to come in." I was too busy watching my friend in the passage to do any interviewing myself. By the time Maria had got the window opened a crowd had collected, who, when they saw Maria's black eyes and tangled hair, guffawed and made some remarks about the old gal getting clawed by her husband. "Excuse me, marm," said the bobby, touching his hat, "but we're come to arrest a gentleman a-living in this house for having travelled in the streets with a boomerang." "Yes, policeman, this is the house he went into; I had him watched," said an old lady in the crowd. I recognised the voice as that of my neighbour in the coach who had called me a wicked young man. "But," says; Maria, in a state of terror at the thought of legal troubles. "But be hanged!" I whispered to Maria. "Just tell them it's all right—the gentleman's inside— and throw them the key. Boomey will get 'em!" Just then I could see Boomey dancing up and down, and waltzing about in the passage, as if he had understood the conversation.

'To see Boomey when the bobby opened that door was particularly fine. He commenced with a gentle kind of tattoo, bouncing round from head to head like the banjo of a Plymouth brother. He evidently just wanted to get the crowd started, so that he could have some fun a-chasing of 'em. "When they did start, the stampede was immense. "Go it, granny" shouted an urchin from an upstairs window to the old woman who was my accuser; "Boomey's a-following!" The basketful of rags that lay in front of the door before the crowd got clear would have run a paper-mill for a month. For a week or two the house was in a state of siege. No one dare venture outside the door without first looking up and down the street. At last we got into the way of travelling by going from house to house. By prearranged signals an open door would be ready for us. If all was clear, we'd make a rush. If Boomey was following, we'd just snap the door to, and wait until he'd gone. One or two tried shot-guns on him, but it wasn't a bit of good—it only seemed to make him more vicious.

'After clearing the town of cats and dogs, Boomey suddenly disappeared. When I was last in Clarenceville I heard that he was raging round a sheep station up in New England, and the contingent had gone up to try their hand on him.

'After my experiences, sir, you needn't tell me that boomerangs won't return; the difficulty is to keep 'em away.'

Colonial Facts and Fictions also contains a story related to an earthquake written by Milne when he was in Wellington, New Zealand, another region of Earth prone to serious earthquake disturbances. The story is called *About Earthquakes* and refers to an incident in a poker game at a local club.

"On one occasion an earth tremor interrupted a poker game held in a club. At the time of the tremor the pool of money had reached a healthy £45. When the tremor came the poker players bolted for safety in all directions. Following the tremor one of the poker players was conspicuous by his absence. He was located shaking and shivering in a cupboard. After a good laugh and a drink they returned to their game only to find the pool of money was missing. They never found it. It was, however, observed that the man that was shaking in the cupboard, at whom they had laughed for being such a jerk, had in fact stayed behind and pocketed the pool, after which he quietly walked into the cupboard. The following week he was seen around town wearing a brand new watch."

It may not be one of the finest of literary works ever published but it is nevertheless a most entertaining read.

Further Reading

Authors References

Baldwin, A. & Alderson, D. M. (1996): A remarkable survivor: a nineteenth century geological trail in Rochdale, England.
Geological Curators Group, Vol. 6., No. 6., pp. 227-231.

Baldwin, W. & Sutcliffe, H S. (1904): *Eoscorpius sparthensis, sp. nov.*, from the Middle Coal Measures of Lancashire.
QJGS., Vol. 60., Part 4, pp. 394-399.

Bernacchi, L. C. & Milne, J. (1908): Earthquakes and other earth movements recorded in the Antarctic regions, 1902-1903.
In National Antarctic Expedition 1901-1904. Physical Observations. London, Royal Society, 1908, pp 37-96.

Davison, C. (1912): The Origin of Earthquakes. *Cambridge University Press.*

Davison, C. The Great Japanese Earthquake of October 28, 1891.
Royal Geographical Society, Vol. 6., No. 1.

Davison, C. (1927): The Founders of Seismology.
Cambridge University Press, London.

Dewey, J. & Byerly, P. (1969): The Early History of Seismometry (to 1900).
Bulletin of the Seismological Society of America, Vol. 59, No. 1., pp. 189-227.

Herbert-Gustar, L. K. & Nott, P. A. (1980): John Milne Father of Modern Seismology. *Paul Norbury Publications Ltd. Tenterden, Kent.*

Hoover, Lou Henry (1912): John Milne, seismologist.
Bulletin of the Seismological Society of America, Vol. 2: pp. 2-7.

McGuire, W. J. (2006): Global risk from extreme geophysical events: threat identification and assessment. *Philosophical Transactions Royal Society. A (2006) 364, 1889 1909 (21 pages). Published at: www.benfieldhrc.org*

Milne, J. (1875): Relics of the Great Auk. *The Field.*

Milne, J. (1878): Across Europe and Asia.
Transactions of the Asiatic Society, Japan, Vol. 7, pp. 1-72.

Milne, J. (1881): The Stone Age in Japan; with Notes on Recent Geological Changes which have taken place.
Journal of the Royal Anthropological Institute of Great Britain and Ireland. Vol. 10, pp. 389-423

Milne, J. (1886): Earthquakes and other earth movements.
Kegan Paul, Trench, & Co., Ltd., London.

Kershaw, M. (1886): Colonial Facts and Fictions - Humorous Sketches.
Chatto and Windus, Piccadilly, London.

Milne, J. (1897): Sub-Oceanic Changes.
Royal Geographical Society, Vol. X., No. 2.

Milne, J. (1898): Seismology.
Kegan Paul, Trench, Trübner & Co. Ltd., London.

Milne, J. (1896 to 1913): Reports to the Seismological Committee.
British Association for the Advancement of Science.

Milne, J. (1899 to 1912): Shide Circulars Nos. 1-27.
British Association for the Advancement of Science.

Schweitzer, J and Lee, W. H. K. (2003): Old seismic bulletins to 1920: a collective heritage from early seismologists. Part XI, 88, pp. 1665 to 17723
International Handbook of Earthquake and Engineering Seismology, Vol. 81B Edited by Lee, Kanamori, Jennings and Kisslinger ISBN: 0-12-440658-0

Additional References
Davison, C. (1921): On the effect of the great Japanese earthquake of 1891 on the seismic activity of the adjoining districts.
Geological Magazine, Vol. IV., pp. 23 - 27.

Davison, C. (1921): A Manual of Seismology. *Cambridge University Press.*

Davison, C. (1924): A History of British Earthquakes.
Cambridge University Press.

Davison, C. (1924): Fusakichi Ōmori and his work on Earthquakes.
Bulletin of the Seismological society of America, 14: pp. 240-255.

Ewing, J. A. (1883): Treatise on Earthquake Measurement.
Memoirs Science Department. Tokio Daigaku, 9, pp. 1–92.

Ewing, J. A. (1886): Earthquake recorders for use in observatories.
Nature. London, 34, pp. 343–344.

Galitzin, Boris Prince. (1914): Vorlesungen über Seismometrie.
Leipzig, Germany.

Gray, T. (1882): A seismometer for registering vertical motion.
Transactions of the Seismological Society, Japan, 3, pp. 137–139.

Gray, T. (1883): On Gray and Milne seismographic apparatus.
Quarterly Journal Geological Society, London., 39, pp. 218–223.

Herbert-Gustar*, L. & Nott, P.A. (1983): Was seismology lucky to acquire John Milne?
USGS Earthquake Information Bulletin, Volume 15, No. 5, pp 164–176.

Hauser, E. C., et al. (2001): 3-D GPR Imaging of the Neodani Fault, Central Japan: 2001.
Symposium on Application of Geophysics to Environmental and Engineering Problems (SAGEEP), 2001 CD Publication GP 1-1, 10p.

Knott, C. G. (1908): The Physics of Earthquake Phenomena.
Oxford, Clarendon Press.

Kotō, B. (1893): The cause of the great earthquake in Central Japan, 1891.
Journal College of Science, Imperial University of Japan, Vol. V., pp. 295–353.

Mallet, R. (1862b): The First Principles of Observational Seismology.
Chapman and Hall, London.

Miyakoshi, K., S. et al. (1988): Activity of the Neodani Fault – Characteristics and Analysis of Fault Movement at Kinbara, Gifu Prefecture.
Report No. U88052 of the Abiko Research Laboratory of the Central Research Institute of the Electric Power Industry (CRIEPI), Japan, 38p

Nott, P.A. (1974): Earthquake Milne and the Isle of Wight. *Vectis, IoW.*

Ōmori, Fusakichi. (1894): On the after-shocks of earthquakes.
Journal College of Science, Imperial University of Japan, Vol. VII., pp. 111-200.

Ōmori, Fusakichi. (1899): Horizontal pendulums for the mechanical registration of seismic and other earth movements.
Journal College of Science, Imperial University of Tokyo 11, pp. 121-145.

Ōmori, Fusakichi. (1901a): Results of horizontal pendulum observations of earthquakes. *Bulletin of the Earthquake Investigation Committee, No. 5.*

Perry, J. & Ayrton, W. E. (1879): On a neglected principle that may be employed in earthquake measurement.
Phil. Magazine Series 5, 8, pp. 30-50.

Seno, T., Sakurai, T. & Stein, S. (1996): Can the Okhotsk plate be discriminated from the North American plate?
Journal of Geophysical Research, Vol. 101 No. B5, Pages 11,305–11,316.

Shaw, J.J. undated. Milne-Shaw Seismograph Handbook.
J.J. Shaw, West Bromwich.

Stonyhurst College Observatory. (1909): Results of Meteorological and Magnetical Observations. *Philip, Son & Nephew Ltd., Liverpool.*

von Rebeur-Paschwitz, E. (1889): The earthquake of Tokio, April 18, 1889.
Nature, London. 40, pp. 294-295.

von Rebeur-Paschwitz, E. (1894a): Description of an apparatus for recording by photography the motions of horizontal pendulums.
Seismological Journal of Japan 3, pp. 35-54.

Wartnaby, J. (1972): Seismological investigations in the nineteenth century, with special reference to the work of John Milne and Robert Mallet, *Unpublished Ph.D. Dissertation, University of London.*

Some publications of John Milne
1874 Notes on the physical features and mineralogy of Newfoundland.
   Q.J.G.S. Vol. 30, pp. 722 - 745.
   Geological notes from the neighbourhood of Cairo.
   Geol. Mag., Vol. 1 (2), pp. 353-362.

1875 Geological notes on the Sinaitic Peninsula Unit, NW Arabia.
Q.J.G.S. Vol. 31, pp. 1 - 28.

1876 Ice and ice-work in Newfoundland.
Geol. Mag., Vol. 3 (2), pp. 303-308, 345-350, 403-410.

1877 On the action of coast ice on an oscillating area.
Q.J.G.S. Vol. 33, pp. 929 - 933 [Abridged].
Considerations on the flotation of icebergs.
Geol. Mag., Vol. 4 (2), pp. 65-71.
On the rocks of Newfoundland. (With Alexander Murray)
Ibid., pp. 251-262.
A Visit to the Volcanoes of Ōshima. *Ibid., pp. 193-9.*
Across Europe and Asia. Travelling Notes.
Ibid., pp. 289-97, 337-46, 389-406, 459-68, 511-18, 557-68;
Vol. 5 (2), pp. 29-37, 62-73.

1878 On the Form of Volcanoes. *Ibid., Vol. 5 (2), pp. 337-45.*

1879 Journey across Europe and Asia.
Trans. Asiatic Soc., Japan, Vol. 7, pp. 1-72.
A Cruise among the Volcanoes of the Kurile Islands.
Geol. Mag., Vol. 6 (2), pp. 337-48.
Further Notes upon the Form of Volcanoes. *Ibid., pp. 506-14.*
Notes on Crystallography and Crystallo-physics.
London: Trübner & Co.
On the Stone Age in Japan. *Rep. Brit. Assoc. Adv. Sci., p. 401.*

1880 Note on the Geographical Distribution of Volcanoes.
Geol. Mag., Vol. 7 (2), pp. 166-70.
Note on the Cooling of the Earth. *Ibid., pp. 99-102.*
Experiments on the Elasticity of Crystals.
Min. Mag., Vol. 3, pp. 178-85.
List of Japanese Minerals, with notes on species which are believed to
be new. *Ibid., pp. 96-100.*
A large Crater (Asosan, in Kiushiu. Japan).
Popular Science Review, Vol. 14, pp. 336-45.
Catalogue, of the Minerals, Rocks, Fossils, Shells, and Casts
contained in the Geological Department of the Imperial College of
Engineering (Kobudai-gakko). *Tokyo.*
Notes on the Stone Implements from Otaru and Hakodate, with a
few general remarks on the prehistoric remains of Japan.
Trans. Asiatic Soc. Japan, Vol. 8, pp. 61-91.
Seismic Science in Japan.
Trans. Seism. Soc. Japan, Vol. 1, pp. 3-37, & Japan Gazette, 1ˢᵗ May, 1880.

Notes on the Recent Earthquakes of Yedo Plain, and their effects on certain buildings. *Trans. Seism. Soc. Japan, Vol. 2, pp. 1-38.*

1881 On Seismic Experiments *(with T. Gray, BSc., F.R.S.E)*
Proc. Royal Society No. 217.

Earthquake Observations and Experiments in Japan
(with T. Gray, BSc., F.R.S.E) Phil. Mag., November.

The Earthquake of 23ʳᵈ Dec. 1880. *The Crysanthemum.*

Notes on the Great Earthquakes of Japan.
Trans. Seim. Soc. Japan, 3, pp. 65-102.

The Stone Age in Japan; with notes on recent geological changes which have taken place.
Journal of the Royal Anthropological Institute of Great Britain & Ireland, Vol. 10, pp. 389–423

1881 & 1892

Investigation of the Earthquake phenomena of Japan.
Twelve Reports Brit. Assoc.

1882 Earthquake Motion. *The Crysanthemum.*

On the Elasticity and Strength Constants of certain Rocks
(With T. Gray, BSc., F.R.S.E) Journal of the Geol. Soc.

A Visit to the Volcano of Ōshima.
Geol. Mag., 2ⁿᵈ Dec., Vol. IV., pp. 193-197, 255.

On the Form of Volcanoes.
Geol. Mag., 2ⁿᵈ Dec. Vol.V., and 2ⁿᵈ Dec. Vol. VI.

Note upon the Cooling of the Earth, &c.
Geol. Mag., 2ⁿᵈ Dec. Vol.VII., p 99.

On Seismic Experiments
(with T. Gray, BSc., F.R.S.E) Trans. Royal Society.

A Large Crater.
Popular Science Review.

The Volcanoes of Japan (a series of articles) *Japan Gazette.*

Earthquake Literature of Japan. (a series of articles) *Japan Gazette.*

Seismology in Japan. *Nature, Oct.*

Earth Movements.
The Times, 12ᵗʰ Oct. See Seismological Society of Japan &c. &c.

1886 Earthquakes and other Earth movements.
Kegan Paul, Trench, & Co., Ltd., London.

Colonial Facts and Fictions - Humorous Sketches.
Chatto & Windus, London.
Published under the pseudonym of Mark Kershaw.

The first Principles of Observational Seismology.

1887 On a Seismic Survey made in Tokyo in 1884 and 1885.
    Trans. Seism. Soc. Japan, Vol. 10, pp. 1-36.
    Earth Tremors in Central Japan. *ibid., Vol. 11., pp. 1-78.*
    Earthquake Effects, Emotional and Moral. *ibid., pp. 91-114.*
    On Construction in Earthquake Countries. *ibid., pp. 115-74.*

1888 Several papers in *Trans. Seism. Soc. Japan, Vol. 12*:
    Effects of Earthquakes on Lower Animals, *pp. 1-4.*
    Modern Pendulum Seismometers, *pp. 22-8.*
    The Gray-Milne Seismograph and other Instruments at Tokyo,
      pp. 33-48.
    Sound Phenomena of Earthquakes, *pp. 53-62.*
    Relative Motion, *pp. 63-6.*
    Movements in Buildings, *pp. 67-76.*
    Seismic Problems, *pp. 107-14.*

1889 Several papers in *Trans. Seism. Soc. Japan, Vol. 13, pt. 1*:
    Earth Tremors in Central Japan, *pp. 7-20.*
    Distribution of Motion in a small Area, *pp. 41-90.*
    Japanese Earthquakes in 1886, pp. *91-132.*
    Vol. 14: Earthquake Motion, *pp. 1-42.*
    Effects on Buildings *pp. 43-83.*
    Information for Builders, *pp. 229-46.*
    Seismic Work in Japan, and On the Vibration of Railway Trains:
      Rep. Brit. Assoc. Adv. Sci., p. 492.
    Building in Earthquake Countries.
      Proc. Inst. C. E., Vol. C.

1890 Papers in *Trans. Seism. Soc. Japan, Vol. 15*:
    Seismometry and Railway Trains, *pp. 23-30*;
    Japanese Earthquakes, *pp. 93-8.*
    Report of Observations for the year 1887, *pp. 99-126*
    Earthquakes in connexion with Electric and Magnetic Phenomena,
      pp. 135-62.

1891 On Phenomena which might be observable if the hypothesis that
    Earthquakes are connected with Electrical Phenomena be entertained.
    Rep. Brit. Assoc. Adv. Sci., p. 583.

1892 (With W. K. Burton) The Great Earthquake in Japan, 1891.
    Yokohama and London [Stanford].
    (With W. K. Burton) The Volcanoes of Japan. Pt. 1: Fujisan.
    Yokohama, Shanghai, Hong-Kong, & Singapore: Kelly and Walsh. (London).

1893 The Miners Handbook.
    Crosby and Lockwood, London

A note on the great earthquake of October 28th 1891.

Seismological Journal of Japan, Vol. 17, pp. 127-151

1895 A Catalogue of 8331 Earthquakes recorded in Japan between 1885 and 1892.

Seism. J. Japan 4, 1367.

Suggestions for a systematic observation in the northern hemisphere of earth waves and vibrations travelling great distances.

1896 The volcanoes of Japan.

Transactions of the Seismological Society of Japan.-Yokohama, Vol. 9., Pt. 2. pp. 539-548.

1898 Seismology. *Kegan Paul, Trench, Trübner & Co. Ltd., London.*

1906 On the installation and working of Milne's Horizontal Pendulum Seismograph. *R.W. Munro, London.*

1911 Catalogue of Destructive Earthquakes.

British Association for the Advancement of Science, Report of the 81st Annual Meeting, Appendix No.1, pp. 649 - 740.

1912 A Catalogue of Destructive Earthquakes A.D. 7 to A.D.

1899, Rep. Brit. Assoc. London, 1911-1912, pp. 549-740.

Vol. 1 Seismic Science in Japan.

35 pages.

Earthquake in Japan of 22nd Feb. 1880.

116 pages, 5 plates, 8 woodcuts.

Vol. 2 Recent Earthquakes of Yeddo, Effects on Buildings, &c.

38 pages, 2 plates and many tables.

Peruvian Earthquake of 9th May, 1887.

47 pages, 2 plates, tables. Constitution, Rules, Officers and Members of the Society, Dec. 1881.

The Great Earthquakes of Japan.

38 pages, 1 plate and many tables.

Vol. 3 Experiments in Observational Seismology.

53 pages, 1 plate, tables.

Horizontal and Vertical Motion in Earthquakes of March 8, 1881.

8 pages, 3 plates.

Vol. 4 None

Vol. 5 Distribution of Seismic Activity in Japan.

30 pages, 1 plate.

Utilisation of Earth's Internal Heat.

12 pages.

Systematic Observation of Earthquakes.

31 pages, 5 plates.

Vol. 6 Earth Pulsations.
Vol. 7 Part 1
 Earth Tremors.
Vol. 7 Part 2
 On 387 Earthquakes observed in North Japan.
  Many plates and maps.
Vol. 8 Seismic Experiments.
Vol. 9 Part 2
 The Volcanoes of Japan.
Vol. 10 A Seismic Survey of Tokio.
Vol. 11 Earth Tremors in Central Japan.
 Earthquake Effects, Emotional and Moral.
 On Construction in Earthquake Countries.
Vol. 12 Effects produced by Earthquakes on the Lower Animals.
 Modern Forms of Pendulum Seismometers.
 The Gray-Milne and other Seismographs.
 On the Sound Phenomena of Earthquakes.
 Relative Motion of neighbouring Points of Ground.
 On the Movements produced in certain Buildings by Earthquakes.
 On Seismic Problems demanding Solutions.
Vol. 13 Part 1
 Earth Tremors in Central Japan.
 On the Distribution of Earthquake Motion within a small area.
 On the Earthquake Observations of 1886.
Vol. 14 Part 2
 Construction in Earthquake Countries.
Vol. 15 Seismometry applied to Railway Trains.
 Diagrams of Earthquakes recorded at the Chirri Kioku in Tokio.
 Earthquake Observations for 1887.
 Catalogue of Earthquakes, 1887 - 1890.
 Earthquakes in connection with Electric and Magnetic Phenomena.
 Construction in Earthquake Countries.
  (Supplementary to Vol. 14).
 A Mantel-piece Seismometer.
 The Chirri Kioku Observations for 1888.
 The Chirri Kioku Observations for 1889.

Web Sites

1. Ainu Museum: *www.ainu-museum.or.jp/english/english.html*

2. British Geological Survey: *www.earthquakes.bgs.ac.uk/*

3. Earthquake Research Institute, Tokyo: *www.eri.u-tokyo.ac.jp/*

4. Earthquake Information Network: *www.eqnet.org/*

5. Incorporated Research Institutions for Seismology: *www.iris.edu/*

6. Isle of Wight: *www.islandbreaks.co.uk/*

7. KVERT - Active volcanoes of Kamchatka and the Kurile Islands: Ebeko: *www.kscnet.ru/ivs/kvert/volcanoes/Ebeko/index_eng.html*

8. Milne Volcano: *www.volcano.si.edu/world/volcano.cfm?vnum=0900-161*

9. Lapworth Museum of Geology, University of Birmingham: *www.lapworth.bham.ac.uk/collections/historical/*

10. Nagasaki University Library: photos of the 'Bakumatsu-Meiji Periods.' *http://hikoma.lb.nagasaki-u.ac.jp/en/index.html*

11. Quaternary Volcanoes of Japan (Geological Survey of Japan): *www.aist.go.jp/RIODB/strata/VOL_JP/*

12. Rochdale: *www.rochdaleonline.org/*

13. Seismological Society of America: *www.seismosoc.org/*

14. Vladimir Kroupnik - History of gold in Russia: *www.goldminershq.com/Vlad.htm/*

15. USGS Earthquake Hazards Programme: *www.earthquake.usgs.gov/*

16. Yutaka Honda: Neodani Fault & Earthquake Museum, Midori. *www.cc.mie-u.ac.jp/~lz00102/cosmos.files/neodani.html*